Jackson's
Geometrical and Engineering Drawing

Fourth Edition

E. JACKSON, M.COLL.H.

Vivian Williams Memorial Prizewinner.
Sometime Lecturer, Teacher Training Dept., Sheffield University.
Sometime Lecturer, Sheffield Education Authority.
Education Officer, Kenya.

GW00585862

Longman

LONGMAN GROUP LIMITED
*Longman House, Burnt Mill, Harlow, Essex CM20 2JE, England
and Associated Companies throughout the World.*

First published 1964
Fourth edition 1977
Fourth impression 1982

ISBN 0 582 33057 2

Printed in Hong Kong by Sheck Wah Tong Printing Press Ltd

Contents

Foreword

This book is intended as a comprehensive textbook for 'O' Level G.C.E. Geometrical and Engineering Drawing, being designed to cover all sections of the syllabus.

Other students should find it useful in preparation for examinations set by the Associated Examining Board, the G1 and G2 of the Ordinary National Certificate, and City and Guilds examinations bearing on engineering and sheet metalwork.

Technical teachers should find the detail and data helpful in framing a four year course, and the many questions and solutions suitable for testing.

The Index has been specially compiled to give quick cross reference to related problems for rapid identification and solution.

London, 1964　　　　EDWARD JACKSON

NOTE TO THE FOURTH EDITION

This edition has been extensively revised to meet the requirements of post 1975 full metrication adopting the recommendations of the BS308: 1972 in the use of ISO metric units to satisfy the needs of Examining Boards whose papers are set wholly in these terms. The Standard has defined details of scales, dimensioning, sectioning, symbols, metal fastenings, conventional representation of engineering components and these points are exemplified in the book diagrams. Other related Standards define the simplified forms, ranges and designations of machine screws and rivets. The revised tables in the Appendices give selected quotes together with SI units, multiples and sub-multiples. The first part of the book deals in detail with plane and solid geometry to sections by inclined planes covering the syllabuses of most Examining Boards in Papers I. First and third angle projections, now used with equal frequency, denoted by symbol or term, are treated fully with many examples and pictorial explanatory diagrams. The second part treats Engineering Drawing for Papers II. Components, assemblies from given parts, completion of work from given part views, production of a working unit to fill a stated purpose, are shown in detail to the standard required by the present trend of examinations. Students and teachers should find the book a comprehensive reference and at the same time, a class or individual working book. We are grateful to the British Standards Institution for permission to reproduce extracts from various British Standards. Copies can be obtained from 101 Pentonville Rd, London N1 9ND.

EDWARD JACKSON, 1977

Part I

PLANE GEOMETRY

Constructions

Areas

Integration

PLANE GEOMETRY

1. Bisection of a Line, by two compass arcs.

2. Right Angle Draw semicircle first; ends of diameter give centres for further arcs.

3. Angle Bisection Three compass arcs give intersection point for line.

4. Trisection of Right Angle Draw quadrant, then arcs from A and B. Join intersections. Note this method is for trisecting a right angle only.

5. Scale of Chords Proceed as in previous diagram; label points 0, 30, 60 and 90. Divide by trial each sectional arc into three, and with 0 as centre draw arcs to meet the straight line 0–90.

6. Use of Scale of Chords The example shows a 50° angle drawn from the scale.

7. Builders' Triangle Draw by compass, inches as units. Note the right angle at junction of sides with units 3 and 4. Made from wooden strips, mm or metres as units, for setting out sites and foundations of buildings.

8. Pythagoras' Theorem 'The area of the square on the hypotenuse of a right-angled triangle is equal to the sum of the squares on the other two sides.' Compare with 7.

9. Equilateral Triangle Draw by compass or 60° setsquare. Equal sides and angles. Unit of hexagon. See 22.

10. Isosceles Triangle Two sides and two angles equal. Three angles of any triangle add up to 180°, i.e. two right angles.

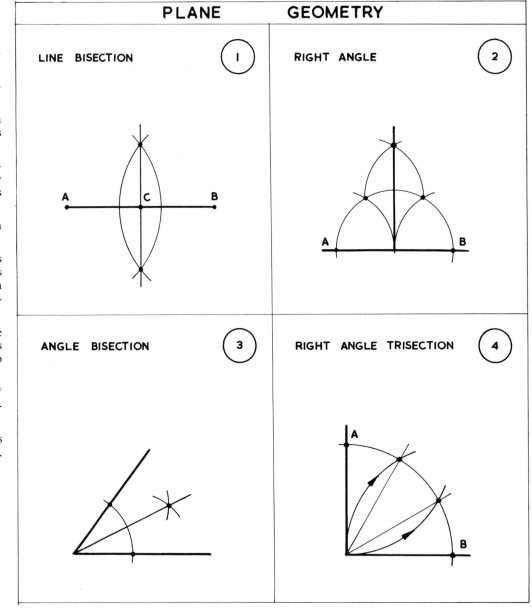

PLANE GEOMETRY

LINE BISECTION ①

RIGHT ANGLE ②

ANGLE BISECTION ③

RIGHT ANGLE TRISECTION ④

PLANE   GEOMETRY

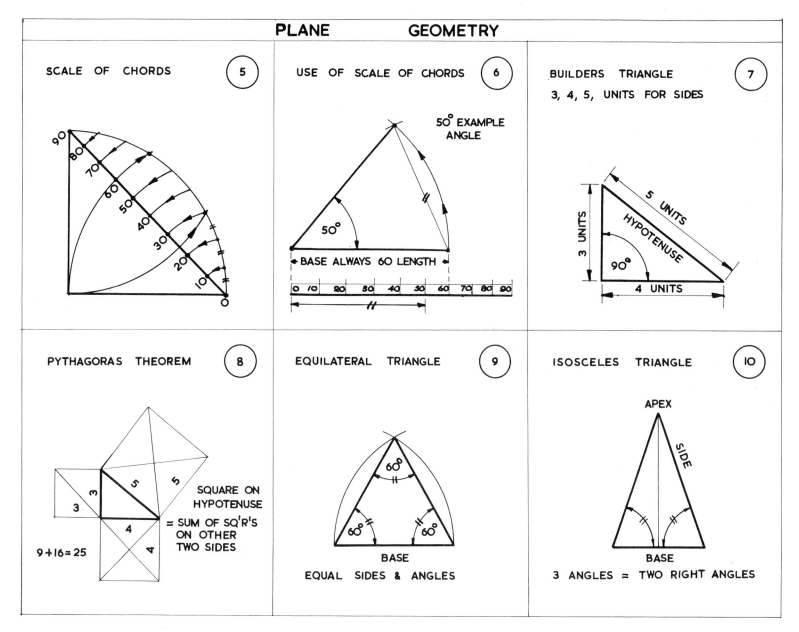

SCALE OF CHORDS (5)

90
80
70
60
50
40
30
20
10
O

USE OF SCALE OF CHORDS (6)

50° EXAMPLE ANGLE

50°

BASE ALWAYS 60 LENGTH

O 10 20 30 40 50 60 70 80 90

BUILDERS TRIANGLE (7)

3, 4, 5, UNITS FOR SIDES

5 UNITS

HYPOTENUSE

3 UNITS

90°

4 UNITS

PYTHAGORAS THEOREM (8)

5
5
3
3
4
4

SQUARE ON HYPOTENUSE = SUM OF SQ'R'S ON OTHER TWO SIDES

9 + 16 = 25

EQUILATERAL TRIANGLE (9)

60°

60°   60°

BASE

EQUAL SIDES & ANGLES

ISOSCELES TRIANGLE (10)

APEX

SIDE

BASE

3 ANGLES = TWO RIGHT ANGLES

11. Right-angled Triangle in Semicircle Any point on the semicircle joined by straight lines to the ends of the diameter, gives a right-angled triangle. Associate with Mean Proportional. See 31.

12. Cyclic Quadrilateral Four corners lie on a circle.

13. Obtuse-angled Triangle One angle more than a right angle.

14. Scalene Triangle All angles acute. No two angles or sides alike.

15. Square Four sides equal in length. Four angles are right angles. Parallelogram. Face of cube (hexadron). Diagonals equal; bisect each other at right angles.

16. Rectangle Parallelogram. Four angles right angles. Opposite sides equal. Adjacent sides unequal. Diagonals bisect but not at right angles.

17. Rhombus Parallelogram. Equal sides. Opposite angles equal. Two acute angles, two obtuse. Diagonals bisect.

18. Rhomboid Parallelogram. Adjacent sides unequal. Opposite sides equal. Diagonals bisect.

19. Trapezium Quadrilateral. Two sides only parallel. Diagonals bisect.

20. Quadrilateral Irregular. May be cyclic.

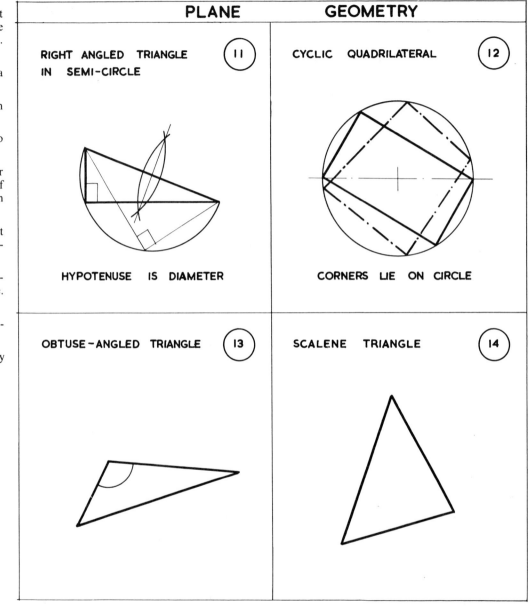

PLANE GEOMETRY

RIGHT ANGLED TRIANGLE IN SEMI-CIRCLE ⑪

HYPOTENUSE IS DIAMETER

CYCLIC QUADRILATERAL ⑫

CORNERS LIE ON CIRCLE

OBTUSE-ANGLED TRIANGLE ⑬

SCALENE TRIANGLE ⑭

PLANE   GEOMETRY

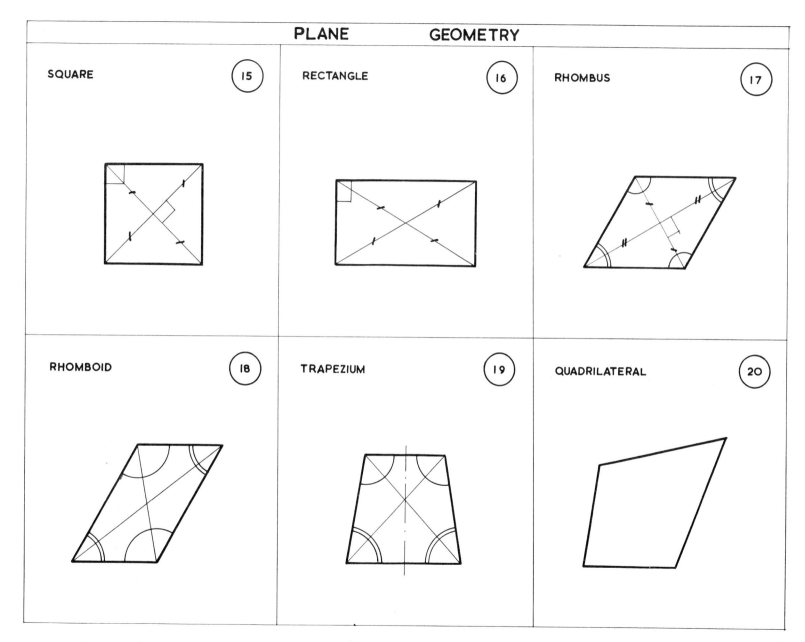

SQUARE (15)

RECTANGLE (16)

RHOMBUS (17)

RHOMBOID (18)

TRAPEZIUM (19)

QUADRILATERAL (20)

5

21. Pentagon Method of drawing regular pentagon, heptagon, nonagon, etc., when one side is given. Draw semicircle with side as radius. Divide by trial into as many parts as the figure has sides, join always to second point: this gives second side. Bisect and draw perpendiculars to these two sides, giving centre of circumscribing circle. Step off rest of sides.

22. Hexagon Regular. Draw with compasses or 60° setsquare. Radius is side of six equilateral triangles. Alternate points give trisection of circle.

23. Octagon Regular eight-sided figure. When drawn in the enclosing square, half length of diagonal gives radius for quadrants which yield points for sides.

24. Trapezion Kite shape. Opposite angles equal. Two sets adjacent sides equal. Diagonals unequal, one is bisected at right angles.

25. Altitude Lines Lines at right angles to base, and passing through apex. Note three positions.

26. Medians Lines drawn from centre of base to apex. Gives centre of gravity. See 102, 103.

27. Alternate Angles Intersecting parallels. 'When a straight line crosses two or more other straight parallel lines, the alternate angles are equal, and the lines are divided proportionately.' See next.

28. Intersecting Parallels Equally spaced parallels are divided equally by a diagonal straight line crossing them. Basis of diagonal scales. See 113 and 114.

29. Third and Fourth Proportionals Draw two lines given, at a suitable angle. With compasses bring the lesser to the greater. Join ends, and draw a parallel to this line through the intersection.

30. Proportionate Division A new line may be divided in the same proportion as a given line by the use of intersecting parallels. Draw the two lines at a suitable angle, join the ends. Draw lines parallel to this line through division points in the given line. The new line is divided now in the same proportion as the given line.

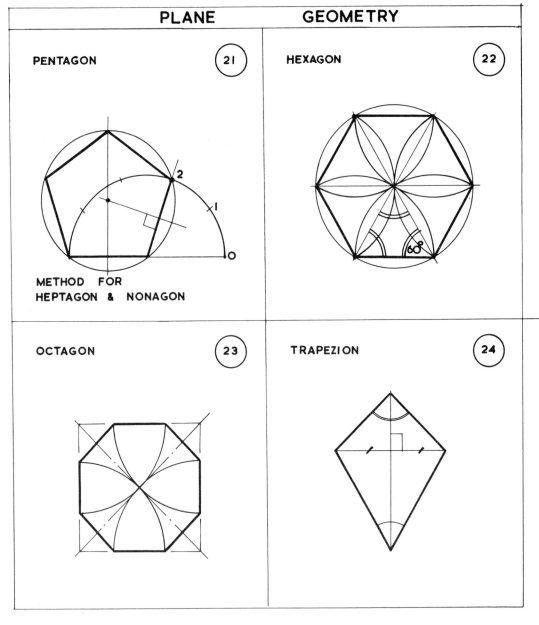

PLANE GEOMETRY

PENTAGON — 21

METHOD FOR HEPTAGON & NONAGON

HEXAGON — 22

OCTAGON — 23

TRAPEZION — 24

PLANE GEOMETRY

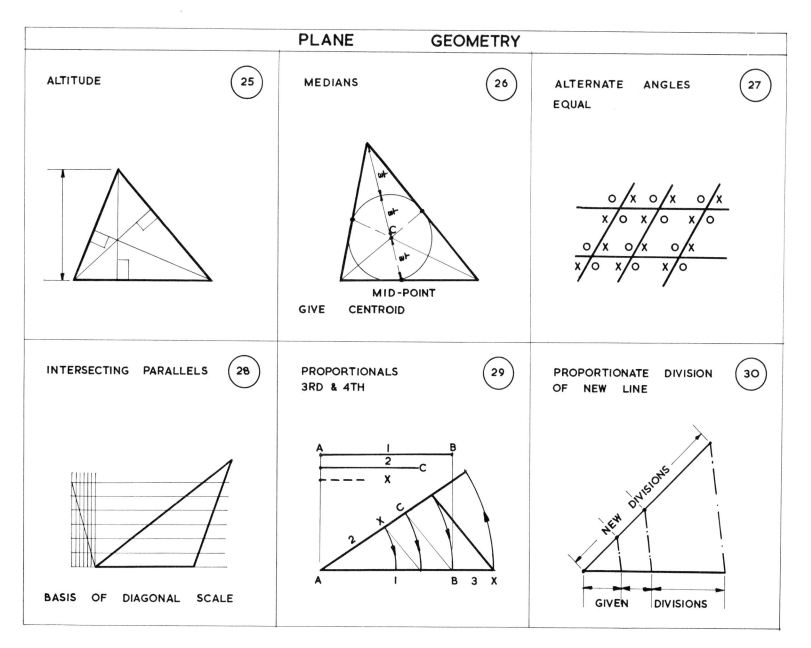

ALTITUDE ⓐ25

MEDIANS ⓐ26

GIVE CENTROID

MID-POINT

ALTERNATE ANGLES ⓐ27
EQUAL

INTERSECTING PARALLELS ⓐ28

BASIS OF DIAGONAL SCALE

PROPORTIONALS ⓐ29
3RD & 4TH

PROPORTIONATE DIVISION ⓐ30
OF NEW LINE

NEW DIVISIONS

GIVEN DIVISIONS

7

31. Mean Proportional Draw a line equal in length to the two given, and on this draw a semicircle. The perpendicular C is the mean proportional.

32. Square of Equal Area When a square equal in area to a given rectangle is to be drawn, the method shown in 31 is used to find the side of the required square.

33. Extreme and Mean Ratio Make O A half A B and perpendicular to AB. Draw hypotenuse, and deduct O A from O B. Remainder is length required.

34. Area of Triangle and Rectangle The area of a triangle is to the area of a rectangle on the same base and altitude as 1:2.

35. Triangles of Equal Area Triangles having the same base and altitude are equal in area but may vary in shape.

36. Quadrilateral reduced to a Triangle of the same Area Draw the diagonal. Draw a line parallel to this line as shown, to an extension of the base. Join to apex. Application of 35.

37. Parts of a Circle Locus of a point which moves at a fixed distance from a fixed point.

38. Centre of a Circle Bisect any two chords. Intersection of perpendiculars gives centre. Conversely a circle can be drawn through three points not in a straight line.

39. Centre Square The tool is set to draw diagonals on the ends of round bars to find the centre.

40. Hexagon in a Circle The radius steps off equally six times into the circumference. Or can be drawn quickly with the 60° setsquare given the length of a side.

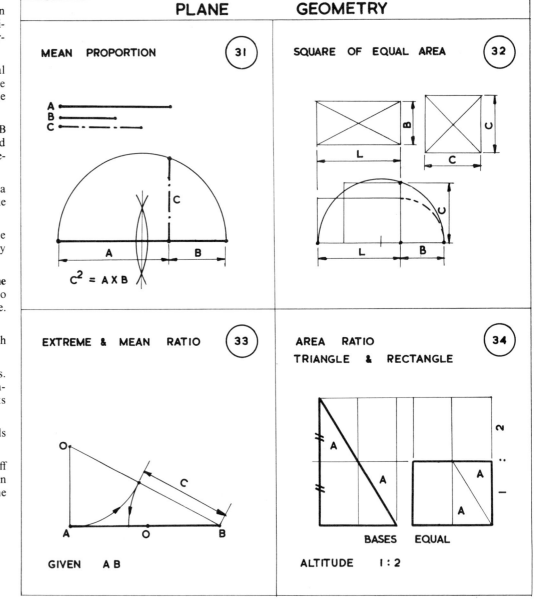

PLANE   GEOMETRY

MEAN PROPORTION   31

SQUARE OF EQUAL AREA   32

$c^2 = A \times B$

EXTREME & MEAN RATIO   33

GIVEN   A B

AREA RATIO
TRIANGLE & RECTANGLE   34

BASES EQUAL

ALTITUDE   1:2

8

PLANE   GEOMETRY

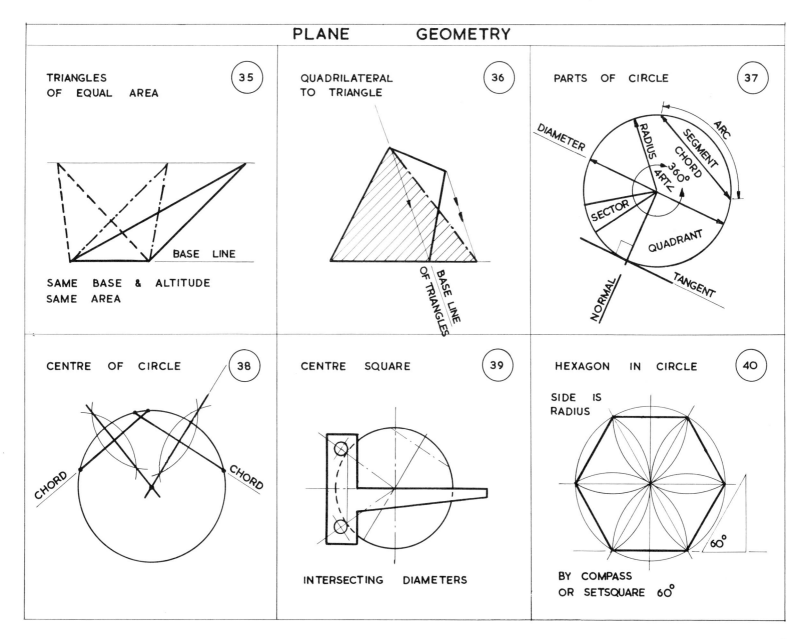

TRIANGLES OF EQUAL AREA (35)

BASE LINE

SAME BASE & ALTITUDE
SAME AREA

QUADRILATERAL TO TRIANGLE (36)

BASE LINE OF TRIANGLES

PARTS OF CIRCLE (37)

DIAMETER
ARC
SEGMENT
RADIUS
CHORD
360°
ARTL
SECTOR
QUADRANT
NORMAL
TANGENT

CENTRE OF CIRCLE (38)

CHORD
CHORD

CENTRE SQUARE (39)

INTERSECTING   DIAMETERS

HEXAGON IN CIRCLE (40)

SIDE IS RADIUS

60°

BY COMPASS
OR SETSQUARE 60°

9

41. Square and Octagon in Circle Draw two diameters at 90°, join points of intersection. Bisect angles for octagon.

42. Pentagon and Heptagon in a circle Divide diameter into same number of parts as sides, swing arcs from ends of diameter, diameter as radius; line through no. 2 point (always). See 21.

43. Simple Tangent to a circle and a point. Join centre and point. Draw semicircle on this line. Draw tangent, note point of intersection. Draw normal. Note right angles formed, tangent perpendicular to radius and normal.

44. Common Tangents to two circles of equal diameters. Join centres. Add radii of circles, and swing arc to cut semicircle drawn on line. Join intersection to centre, and draw parallel line, which is interior tangent. Exterior tangent is line drawn parallel to line joining centres.

45. Exterior Common Tangents to two unequal circles. Join centres, and draw semicircle. Deduct radii, and draw small circle in larger. The problem is now a simple tangent as in 43. Note the parallels and right angles.

46. Interior Common Tangents to two unequal circles. Join centres and draw semicircle thereon. Add radii, and draw circle to cut semicircle. Join intersections to centre of smaller circle. Tangent is parallel to this line, R_2 distance.

47. Touching Circles Deduct radii for internal circle, and add for externally touching circles. Notice that intersections are on line joining centres (or produced), tangent is at right angles to this line; normal is continuation of the line. Much used in machine drawing. See 65 and 67.

48 Segment to contain a given angle on a given straight line. Draw the line, draw angle at end as shown. Draw perpendicular to angle line. Bisect the given line and draw perpendicular. From this centre draw circle. Angle line produced is tangent. This construction also solves problems of touching circles and triangle construction. See 69 and 72.

49. Circle in an Angle Draw the angle. Draw parallels to the arms of the angle at a distance equal to the radius of the given circle. Point of intersection is the centre for the circle. See 61 and 62.

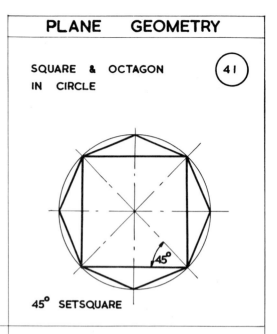

SQUARE & OCTAGON IN CIRCLE ④1

45°

45° SETSQUARE

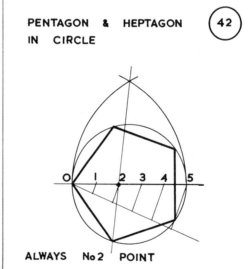

PENTAGON & HEPTAGON IN CIRCLE ④2

O 1 2 3 4 5

ALWAYS No 2 POINT

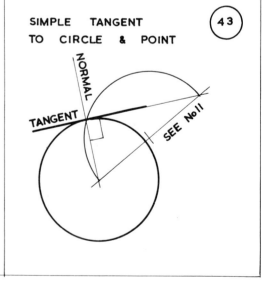

SIMPLE TANGENT TO CIRCLE & POINT ④3

NORMAL

TANGENT

SEE No 11

PLANE GEOMETRY

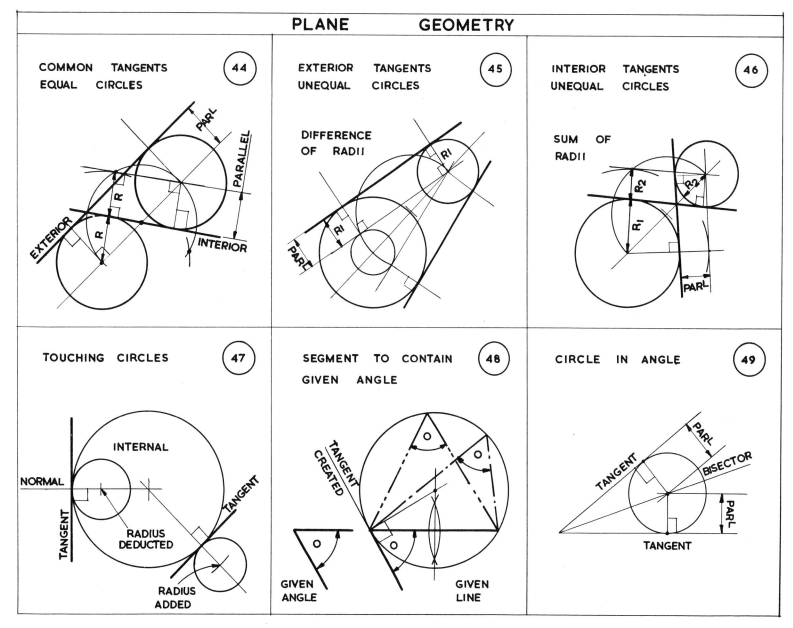

COMMON TANGENTS EQUAL CIRCLES (44)

EXTERIOR PARL PARALLEL R R R INTERIOR

EXTERIOR TANGENTS UNEQUAL CIRCLES (45)

DIFFERENCE OF RADII

R1 R1 PARL

INTERIOR TANGENTS UNEQUAL CIRCLES (46)

SUM OF RADII

R2 R2 R1 PARL

TOUCHING CIRCLES (47)

INTERNAL NORMAL TANGENT RADIUS DEDUCTED TANGENT RADIUS ADDED

SEGMENT TO CONTAIN GIVEN ANGLE (48)

TANGENT CREATED O O O O GIVEN ANGLE GIVEN LINE

CIRCLE IN ANGLE (49)

TANGENT PARL BISECTOR PARL TANGENT

11

50. Touching Circles in an Angle Proceed as in 49. Draw a tangent, i.e. a line at right angles to the bisector of the angle where it cuts the circle. Join the centre and end of the tangent. Draw a second tangent at 2. A line parallel to the first radius to give the centre for the second circle. Repeat for any number of touching circles.

51. Circle in a Triangle Bisect the angles, the point of intersection is the incentre. A perpendicular from a side passing through the incentre gives the radius of the circle.

52. Triangle in a Circle Bisect the sides and erect perpendiculars. A circle may be drawn passing through the points of the triangle.

53. Escribed Circle of a Triangle Extend sides of triangle, bisect angles so formed to give the centre of the circle. A perpendicular from the side extension passing through the centre gives the radius of the circle.

54. Three Touching Circles in a Triangle Bisect angles to give three sub triangles, the centres of which are again given by the bisection. See 51.

55. Three Circles in a Triangle Draw medians, bisect angles, obtain radius from perpendiculars from side to centre. Notice the similar triangle joining the centres. Notice how the median becomes a tangent to the circle.

56. Six Circles in a Hexagon Divide the hexagon into its six basic equilateral triangles, see 22 and 40. Bisect angles to give centres.

57. Three Circles in a Semicircle Draw the three sides of the enclosing hexagon, tangentially to the semicircle. Now divide into three equilateral triangles, and treat as in 56.

58. Touching Circles in a Semicircle Draw two 45° lines tangentially to the semicircle and the perpendicular from the diameter. This gives two right-angled triangles, and circles may be drawn in using bisectors and perpendiculars, see 51. A square based on the two centres and the middle point of the diameter gives the centre for the small circle. Notice other squares and tangents.

PLANE GEOMETRY

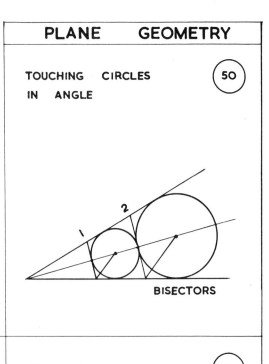

TOUCHING CIRCLES IN ANGLE ⑤⓪

2

1

BISECTORS

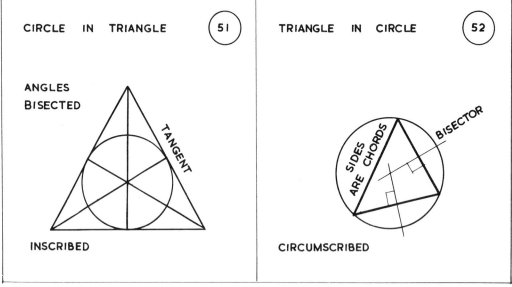

CIRCLE IN TRIANGLE ⑤①

ANGLES BISECTED

TANGENT

INSCRIBED

TRIANGLE IN CIRCLE ⑤②

SIDES ARE CHORDS

BISECTOR

CIRCUMSCRIBED

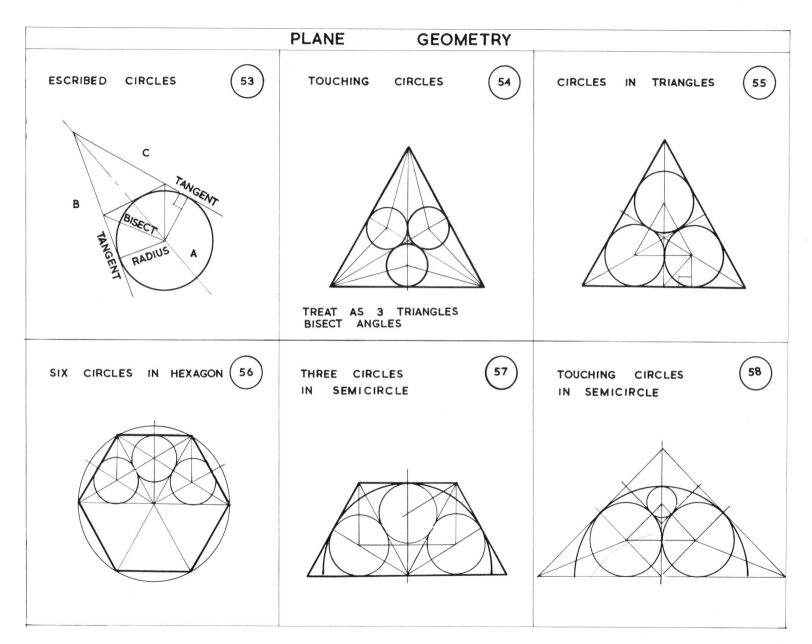

PLANE GEOMETRY

ESCRIBED CIRCLES (53)

C

B

TANGENT

BISECT

TANGENT

RADIUS

A

TOUCHING CIRCLES (54)

TREAT AS 3 TRIANGLES
BISECT ANGLES

CIRCLES IN TRIANGLES (55)

SIX CIRCLES IN HEXAGON (56)

**THREE CIRCLES
IN SEMICIRCLE** (57)

**TOUCHING CIRCLES
IN SEMICIRCLE** (58)

13

59. Three Touching Circles given the radii. R_1 plus R_2; R_1 plus R_3; R_2 plus R_3 gives the sides of a triangle, which has, at the apices, the centres of the three circles. Note the tangency. This is an important method for finding the centres of wheels, gears and shafts, etc. See 68.

60. Circle in a Quadrant This is part of a larger figure, i.e. four touching circles in a larger circle. By drawing a tangent to the mid point of the arc where the bisector intersects, the enclosing triangle is seen.

61. Circle meeting a Straight Line Locus of a point. Lines parallel to the arms of an angle at a distance equal to the radius of the circle. Much used in engineering drawing when connecting arcs and fillets are to be shown.

62. Circles joining Lines This locus of a point which moves at a given distance round the perimeter of an object or shape. Notice the use of perpendiculars and tangency. Much used in engineering drawing. See 49.

63. Touching Circles Method of obtaining radius and centre of an arc to join two given circles and to pass through a point P by using a constructional circle equal in diameter to the given circles. Join the centres, erect a perpendicular bisector to cut the centre line giving c and Pc the length of the radius.

64. Touching Circles Second case using the above method to find centres and radii of inner and outer joining arcs. Two typical shapes for cover plates are shown needing such construction.

65. Touching Circles Application of 44. Add or subtract radii to give length of constructive arc. Can only be used on internally or externally touching circles.

66. Joining Arcs To find the centre of an unknown circle which has to touch two lines and pass through a point, the line of angle bisection should be drawn, and a larger trial circle drawn. Draw a line passing through the point and the angle. Join the intersection of this line with the trial circle to the centre of this circle. Parallels to this line passing through the given point will give the centre of the required circle.

67. Joining Arcs The diagram shows two circles internally connected by large arcs which are part of a large enclosing circle. Subtraction of the radii from the large radius finds the centres of the enclosing circles.

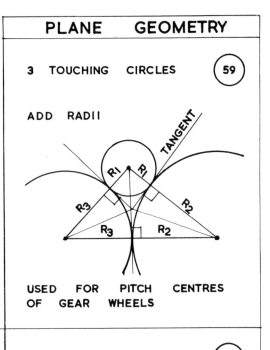

3 TOUCHING CIRCLES (59)

ADD RADII

USED FOR PITCH CENTRES OF GEAR WHEELS

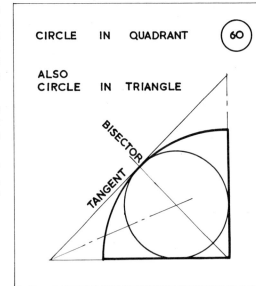

CIRCLE IN QUADRANT (60)

ALSO CIRCLE IN TRIANGLE

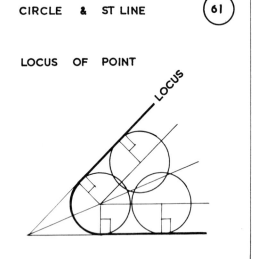

CIRCLE & ST LINE (61)

LOCUS OF POINT

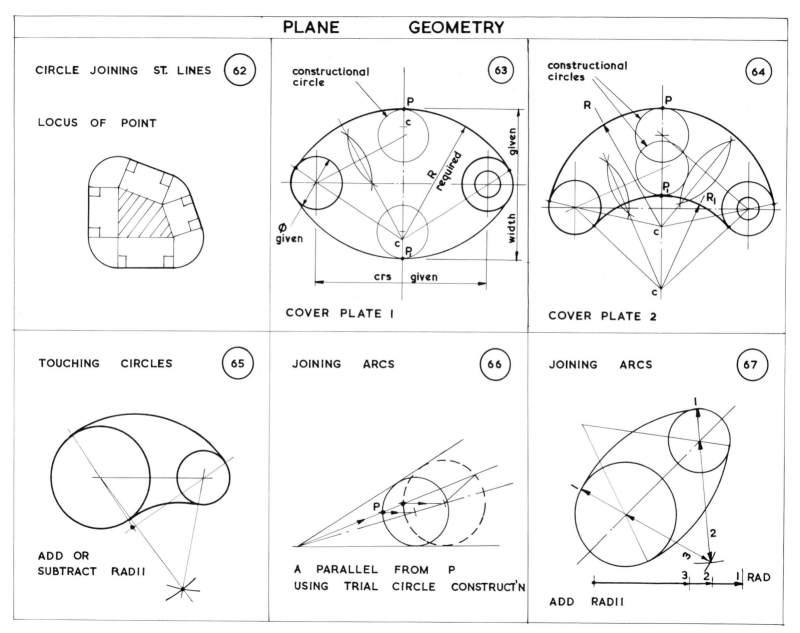

PLANE GEOMETRY

CIRCLE JOINING ST. LINES (62)

LOCUS OF POINT

constructional circle (63)

Ø given

crs given

COVER PLATE 1

constructional circles (64)

R

R_l

COVER PLATE 2

TOUCHING CIRCLES (65)

ADD OR SUBTRACT RADII

JOINING ARCS (66)

P

A PARALLEL FROM P USING TRIAL CIRCLE CONSTRUCT'N

JOINING ARCS (67)

3 | 2 | 1 RAD

ADD RADII

15

68. Three Touching Circles Sum of radii gives the triangle of the centres. See 59.

69. Double Angle at Centre The angle at the centre is twice that at perimeter. Subtended.

70. Direction by Compass In land or sea survey or measuring, instructions of angular movement are given by compass bearing. Cardinal points of North, South, East and West and subdivided as shown, giving 32 compass points.

71. Direction and Distance An example of plotting an area by compass directions. Distance may be stated in m.p.h. or knots (sea speed), or kilometres per hour, held for a certain time period. 30 k.p.h. for $2\frac{1}{2}$ hours gives a distance of 75 km.

72. Angles in Segments Angles in the same segment are equal. Angle in a lesser segment is obtuse. Angle in a semicircle is a right angle. See 11.

73. Area of a Square Graphic method of showing that the height units times the breadth units, give area in square measure.

74. Area of Rectangle Same rule applies.

75. Area of Parallelogram Base times altitude.

76. Area of Triangle $\frac{1}{2}$(base × altitude). Notice that the diagram also stresses that triangles on the same base and of the same altitude have the same area, though may be not the same shape. See 35.

77. Area of a Trapezium can be found by applying 73, 75 and 76. Division into triangles and parallelograms, sum of such divisions.

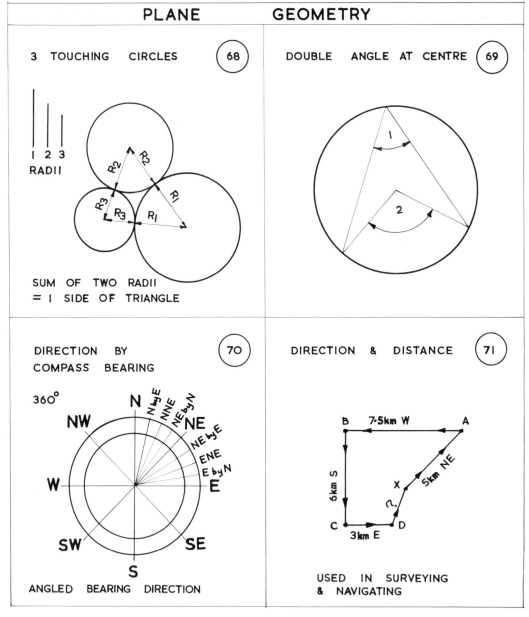

3 TOUCHING CIRCLES 68

1 2 3 RADII

SUM OF TWO RADII = 1 SIDE OF TRIANGLE

DOUBLE ANGLE AT CENTRE 69

DIRECTION BY COMPASS BEARING 70

360°

ANGLED BEARING DIRECTION

DIRECTION & DISTANCE 71

USED IN SURVEYING & NAVIGATING

PLANE GEOMETRY

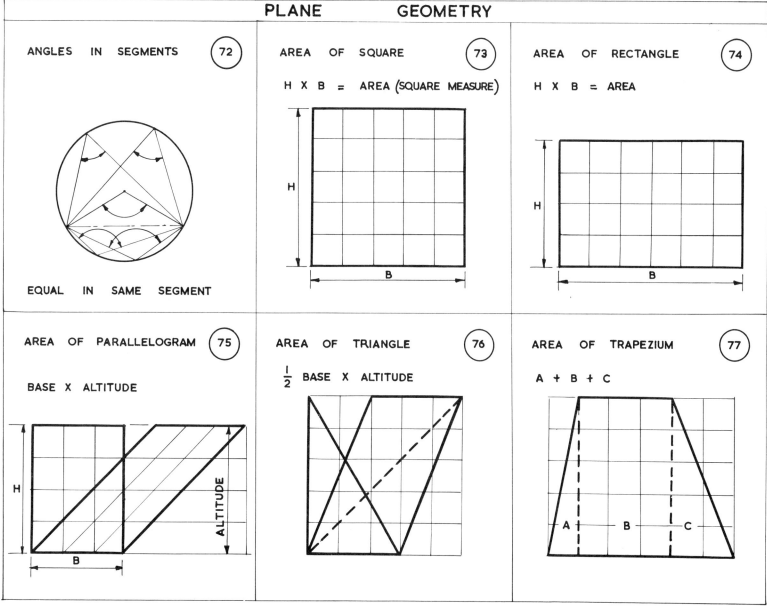

ANGLES IN SEGMENTS (72)

EQUAL IN SAME SEGMENT

AREA OF SQUARE (73)

H X B = AREA (SQUARE MEASURE)

H

B

AREA OF RECTANGLE (74)

H X B = AREA

H

B

AREA OF PARALLELOGRAM (75)

BASE X ALTITUDE

H

B

ALTITUDE

AREA OF TRIANGLE (76)

$\frac{1}{2}$ BASE X ALTITUDE

AREA OF TRAPEZIUM (77)

A + B + C

A   B   C

78. Quadrilateral or Polygon, Regular or Irregular Reduce to one triangle, or by division as before; or reduce to square of equal area. See 36.

79. Area of an Irregular Figure Calculate by squared paper, or by Mid-ordinates Rule. Width of strip times sum of mid-ordinates.

80. Simpson's Rule for the Area of an Irregular Figure The formula is shown.

81. Area of a Circle By formula $3\frac{1}{7}$ times radius squared. Diagram shows how sectors can be laid head and tail to form parallelogram, area of which is base times height.

82. Square Equal in Area to Circle By the solution of 81, draw a rectangle $3\frac{1}{7}$ times R long, and R high. Convert this by the Mean Proportional Method, 31 and 32, to a square of equal area.

83. Circle Equal to Two Circles By Pythagoras' method, draw a right-angled triangle with base equal to one diameter, and the height equal to the other diameter. The hypotenuse gives the diameter of the required circle.

84. Squares and Roots The diagram shows how to obtain the square root of 2, 3, 4, etc. Lengths of the hypotenuse should be measured accurately on a diagonal scale. See 110.

85. Enlargement of Plane Figures The diagram shows that if the length and breadth of a square are increased, then the *area* increases as the square of the increase. For example, an increase of 1 to 4 of the side gives 16 as the area. Draw the line in the diagram to show that an increase of 1 to $1\frac{1}{2}$ gives increase in area to $2\frac{1}{4}$. Notice that fractional decreases are by root: $\frac{1}{8}$ side decrease would yield $\frac{1}{64}$.

86. Linear reduction of Irregular Figures For convenience, the base is reduced by proportionate measuring, parallels to the sides meeting diagonals give the required shape. Increases may be made using this method.

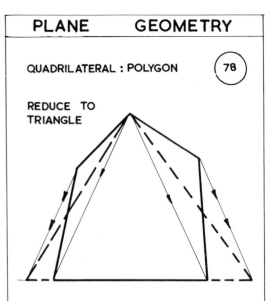

PLANE   GEOMETRY

QUADRILATERAL : POLYGON   (78)

REDUCE TO TRIANGLE

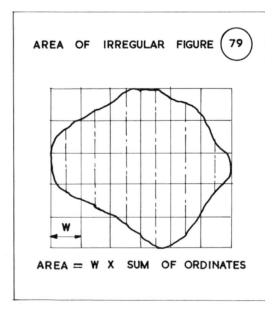

AREA OF IRREGULAR FIGURE (79)

AREA = W X SUM OF ORDINATES

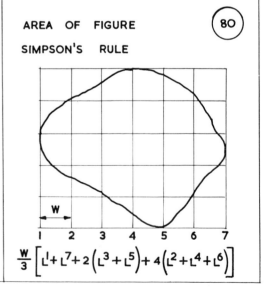

AREA OF FIGURE (80)

SIMPSON'S RULE

$$\frac{W}{3}\left[L^1 + L^7 + 2\left(L^3 + L^5\right) + 4\left(L^2 + L^4 + L^6\right)\right]$$

PLANE GEOMETRY

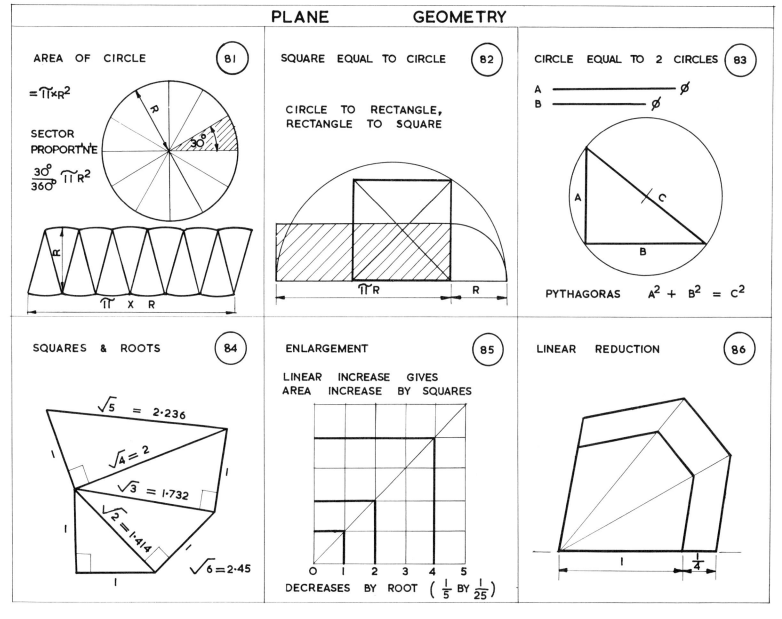

AREA OF CIRCLE (81)

$= \pi \times R^2$

SECTOR
PROPORT'NE

$\dfrac{30^\circ}{360^\circ} \, \pi R^2$

$\pi \times R$

SQUARE EQUAL TO CIRCLE (82)

CIRCLE TO RECTANGLE,
RECTANGLE TO SQUARE

πR R

CIRCLE EQUAL TO 2 CIRCLES (83)

A ——————— ⌀
B ——————— ⌀

PYTHAGORAS $A^2 + B^2 = C^2$

SQUARES & ROOTS (84)

$\sqrt{5} = 2.236$
$\sqrt{4} = 2$
$\sqrt{3} = 1.732$
$\sqrt{2} = 1.414$
$\sqrt{6} = 2.45$

ENLARGEMENT (85)

LINEAR INCREASE GIVES
AREA INCREASE BY SQUARES

O 1 2 3 4 5

DECREASES BY ROOT $\left(\dfrac{1}{5} \text{ BY } \dfrac{1}{25} \right)$

LINEAR REDUCTION (86)

1      $\dfrac{1}{4}$

19

87. Increase by Ratio and Pole Any convenient point near the middle of the figure can be taken, and lines to the corners drawn. One of these lines is divided or increased in the desired ratio, and lines parallel to the sides drawn to complete the new figure.

88. Increase in Area may be done working on the base line. In the diagram the base has been extended to the left, and semicircles drawn in the ratio. A perpendicular intersects the semicircles, giving points from which the new point for the new figure may be completed as in 86. Decreases may be made using this method.

89. Enlargement or Reduction of figures may be made from an external point as shown in the diagram. Lines radiate from the point through salient points of the figure to the required size.

90. Isosceles Triangle Given altitude and perimeter. Draw base A B equal to perimeter, bisect and draw centre height line. Join A C and B C. Bisect B C and draw perpendicular to cut base line in D. Join C D, and complete the required triangle.

91. Trisection of Area of Triangle from point in one side. Divide the side into three (30). Join P to apex, and draw lines parallel to this line through 1 and 2 in the base. From the points of intersection B and C draw lines of division to the point.

92. Triangle divided by Lines Parallel to Base Draw semicircle on side. Divide side into number of required equal spaces, erect a perpendicular at each point to cut the semicircle. With 0 as centre swing an arc from each intersection to the side. Draw lines parallel to the base through these points. See 31.

20

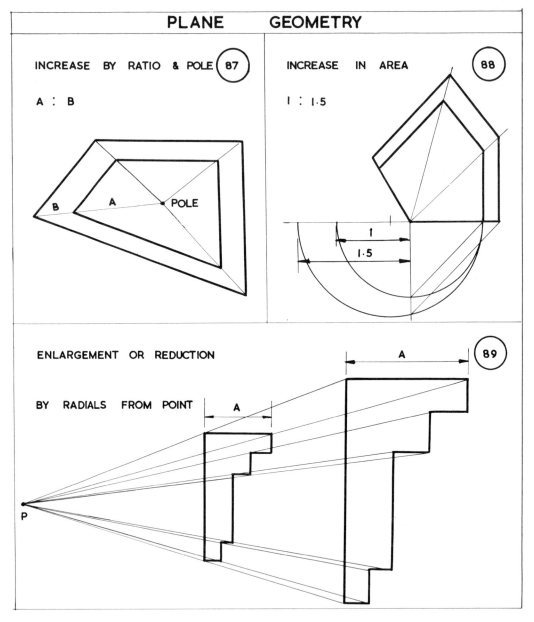

PLANE   GEOMETRY

INCREASE BY RATIO & POLE 87

A : B

B   A   POLE

INCREASE   IN   AREA   88

1 : 1·5

1

1·5

ENLARGEMENT OR REDUCTION   89

BY   RADIALS   FROM   POINT

A

A

P

PLANE GEOMETRY

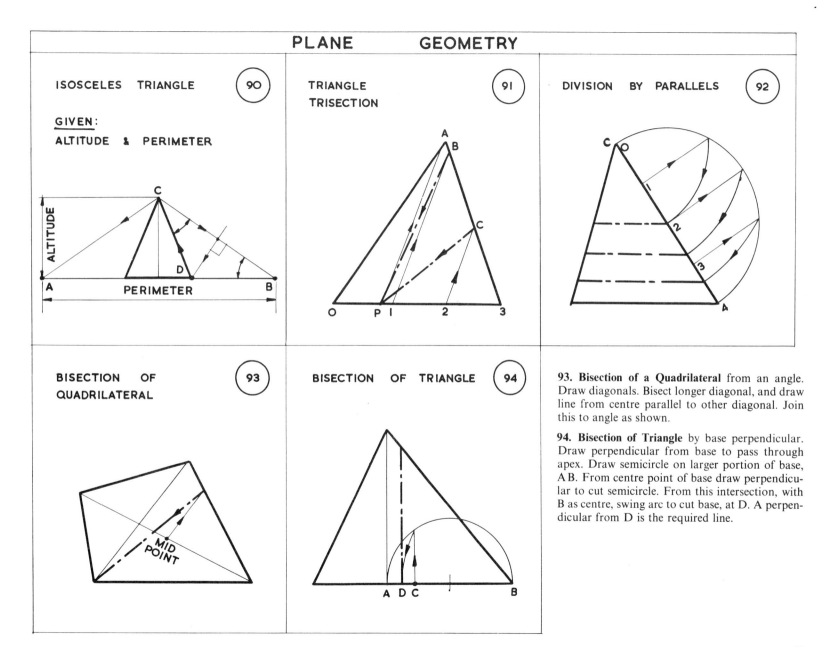

ISOSCELES TRIANGLE (90)

GIVEN:

ALTITUDE & PERIMETER

TRIANGLE TRISECTION (91)

DIVISION BY PARALLELS (92)

BISECTION OF QUADRILATERAL (93)

BISECTION OF TRIANGLE (94)

93. Bisection of a Quadrilateral from an angle. Draw diagonals. Bisect longer diagonal, and draw line from centre parallel to other diagonal. Join this to angle as shown.

94. Bisection of Triangle by base perpendicular. Draw perpendicular from base to pass through apex. Draw semicircle on larger portion of base, A B. From centre point of base draw perpendicular to cut semicircle. From this intersection, with B as centre, swing arc to cut base, at D. A perpendicular from D is the required line.

95. Triangle Given perimeter, altitude and vertex angle. Construct the apex angle, make arms equal to half perimeter. Draw the constructional arcs as shown, and construct a common tangent giving the third side of the triangle.

96. Reduction of Re-entrant Polygon to triangle of equal area. Join A to B. Through C draw a parallel CD. Draw DE, and through A draw a parallel AF. Join F to E. Refer to 36.

97. Reduction of Polygon to Square of equal area. Reduce polygon to triangle by method in 36. Bisect the altitude to give point to draw rectangle of equal area to triangle, see 34. By mean proportional method in 31, 32, draw the square required.

98. Polygon to Triangle on Common Base and Angle If the diagram is turned so that A B is horizontal, it will be seen that this is 36 with two steps.

99. Triangles of Equal Area, diminished altitude. Draw perpendicular mark off new altitude. Join this to base angles, and draw parallels to these lines from the old apex. Join new apex to new base points. This problem is 36 in reverse.

100. New Triangle of Equal Area Extend base to new length, join to apex. From old base angle, draw parallel to this line. Point of intersection gives new side of required triangle. See 36.

101. Rectangles of Equal Area Extend base of rectangle to new length, and erect perpendicular to height of rectangle. Draw diagonal. Where this intersects the side, draw parallel to base, giving required rectangle. Use in reverse, also.

102. Re-entrant Quadrilateral Divide the sides of the quadrilateral into three equal parts. Join the appropriate points to give the rectangle; intersection of the diagonals gives the centre of gravity (balance point of figure).

103. Division of Quadrilateral by Line through Centre Draw one diagonal, and draw medians in the two triangles thus formed. Join the two centres of gravity thus found. Draw the other diagonal of the quadrilateral, and draw the medians in these other two major triangles. Join their centres of gravity. Where the two lines cross is the centre of gravity of the whole quadrilateral. Any line drawn through this final centre of gravity will cut area into two equal parts.

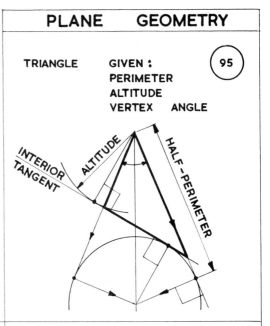

PLANE GEOMETRY

TRIANGLE GIVEN: **95**
PERIMETER
ALTITUDE
VERTEX ANGLE

INTERIOR TANGENT   ALTITUDE   HALF-PERIMETER

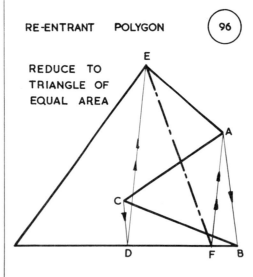

RE-ENTRANT POLYGON **96**

REDUCE TO TRIANGLE OF EQUAL AREA

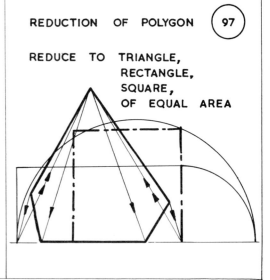

REDUCTION OF POLYGON **97**

REDUCE TO TRIANGLE, RECTANGLE, SQUARE, OF EQUAL AREA

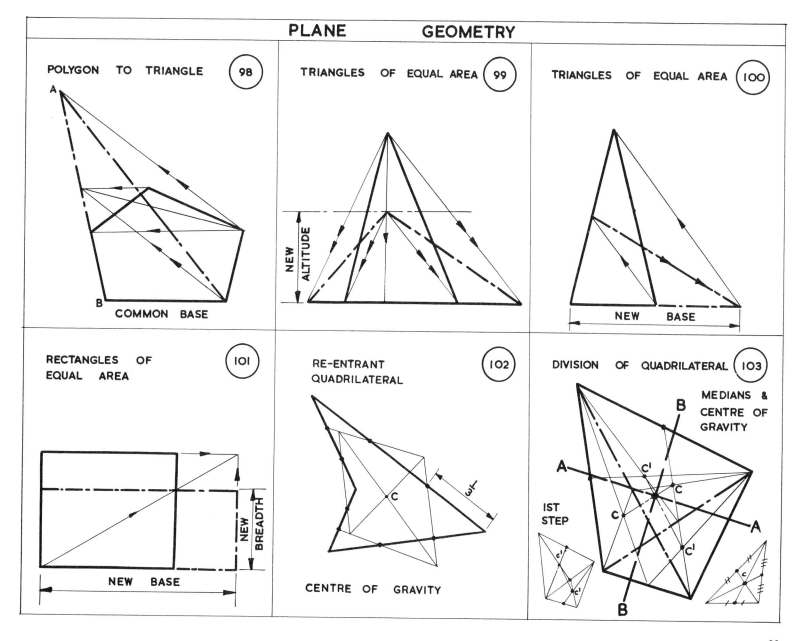

PLANE GEOMETRY

POLYGON TO TRIANGLE (98)

A

B COMMON BASE

TRIANGLES OF EQUAL AREA (99)

NEW ALTITUDE

TRIANGLES OF EQUAL AREA (100)

NEW BASE

RECTANGLES OF EQUAL AREA (101)

NEW BREADTH

NEW BASE

RE-ENTRANT QUADRILATERAL (102)

C

CENTRE OF GRAVITY

DIVISION OF QUADRILATERAL (103)

MEDIANS & CENTRE OF GRAVITY

B

A

C'

C

A

C'

C'

C

IST STEP

c'

c'

c

B

23

104. Diameter from Circumference Draw base equal to given circumference. Bisect and draw semicircle. Cut semicircle in 1 by arc from A, radius half-perimeter. Draw perpendicular giving point 2. Draw arc from 2 with radius 1–2 cutting base in 3. 03 is the approx diameter of the circle. The diameter can be found by dividing the circumference by $3\frac{1}{7}$.

105. Circumference from Diameter Draw a semicircle on the given diameter. Erect perpendicular, and make equal to 3 diameters. Draw 30° angle in semicircle, and draw short perpendicular to cut original diameter. Join as shown, giving approximate circumference. The circumference may be found by multiplying the diameter by $3\frac{1}{7}$.

106. Arc Equal to Line Draw the given line. Divide into 4 parts. Erect perpendicular at B, and draw arc to given radius to touch line tangential at B. Draw arc to cut the first arc at C, radius $\frac{3}{4}$ of the line length.

107. Line Equal to Arc Draw the given arc CB. Draw a tangent AB to the arc, making the extension equal to $\frac{1}{2}$ AB. Draw an arc from P, radius CP, to cut the tangent. AB is the straight line approximately equal to the arc.

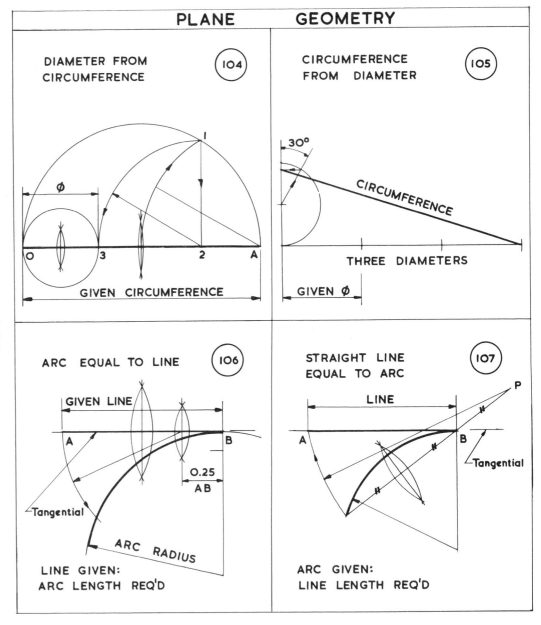

PLANE GEOMETRY

DIAMETER FROM CIRCUMFERENCE ④104

GIVEN CIRCUMFERENCE

CIRCUMFERENCE FROM DIAMETER ⑤105

30°

CIRCUMFERENCE

THREE DIAMETERS

GIVEN Ø

ARC EQUAL TO LINE ⑥106

GIVEN LINE

A   B

0.25 AB

Tangential

ARC RADIUS

LINE GIVEN: ARC LENGTH REQ'D

STRAIGHT LINE EQUAL TO ARC ⑦107

LINE

P

A   B

Tangential

ARC GIVEN: LINE LENGTH REQ'D

108. Triangle Given base, opposite angle and altitude. Draw base line, and base angle below line. Erect a perpendicular at the intersection as shown. Bisect the base line, erect a perpendicular. The intersection forms the centre for the circle shown. Draw the altitude line parallel to the base cutting the circle. Join up the points of the triangle. Compare this with 48.

109. Triangle Given base, base angle and perimeter. Draw the base line, construct the base angle. Extend side to length perimeter less base. Join to base and bisect. Draw perpendicular cutting side. Join up to give triangle. Compare with 102.

110. Triangle Given base, altitude and perimeter. Draw base A B. Bisect and draw perpendicular. Make D E equal to half-perimeter less A B. With centre A and radius D E, cut D F in F. With centre D, and radii D E and D F, draw arcs. Draw the altitude line parallel to the base line, cutting the D F arc. Draw the radial line from D, to cut the outer arc. The final perpendicular from the point of intersection in the outer arc to the altitude line as shown, enables the triangle to be completed.

111. Area Ratio Increase and decrease. Draw the base line, extend to new proportion. Draw semicircles as shown, and cut these by a perpendicular. From the intersections, draw the parallels giving the new length of base lines.

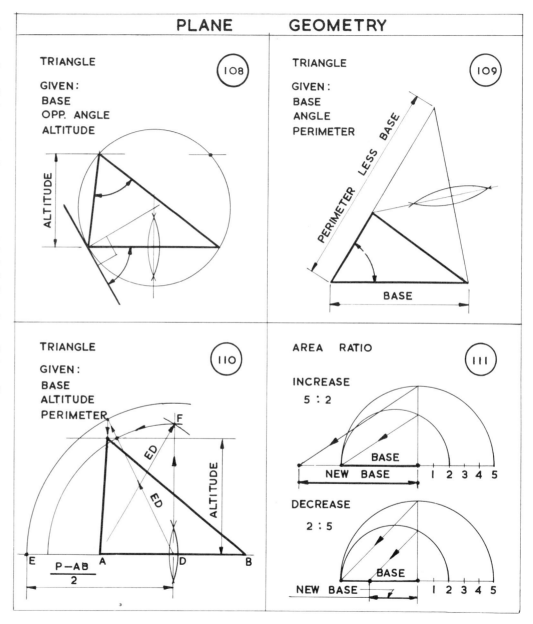

PLANE   GEOMETRY

TRIANGLE   108

GIVEN:
BASE
OPP. ANGLE
ALTITUDE

ALTITUDE

TRIANGLE   109

GIVEN:
BASE
ANGLE
PERIMETER

PERIMETER LESS BASE

BASE

TRIANGLE   110

GIVEN:
BASE
ALTITUDE
PERIMETER

F
ED
ED
ALTITUDE
E   P—AB   A   D   B
    2

AREA   RATIO   111

INCREASE
5 : 2

BASE
NEW BASE   1 2 3 4 5

DECREASE
2 : 5

BASE
NEW BASE   1 2 3 4 5

112. Graphical Integration of Areas The area of a figure may be found graphically by the following method (instead of by calculation, see 79, 80): Draw the figure and the two axes OX and OY. Divide the figure by lines perpendicular to OX; A, B, etc. (The divisions may be closer where the figure changes shape rapidly.)

Draw mid-ordinates in the divisions; 1, 2, 3 etc. Reduce the figure to the axis OX as shown in the middle diagram, the height of the mid-ordinates and divisions remain the same; where the figure is pierced, the two bits of length are added. Project the points of the mid-ordinates, 1, 2, 3 etc., to the OY axis. Fix a pole P on the extended line of OX, and join the projection points on OY to P.

Draw the third diagram shown. The widths of the divisions remain the same, the angle of the line in the first space Oa is equal to that from P to the projection point of 1 in the middle diagram. In the second space, the line ab is the same angle as that of the line P to the projection point of 2. Proceed until the final height point on the last division H is obtained.

The area of the original figure is equal to that of the rectangle contained by the pole distance and the final height, i.e. PO × Hg.

The three diagrams may be superimposed in the one diagram to save space and time.

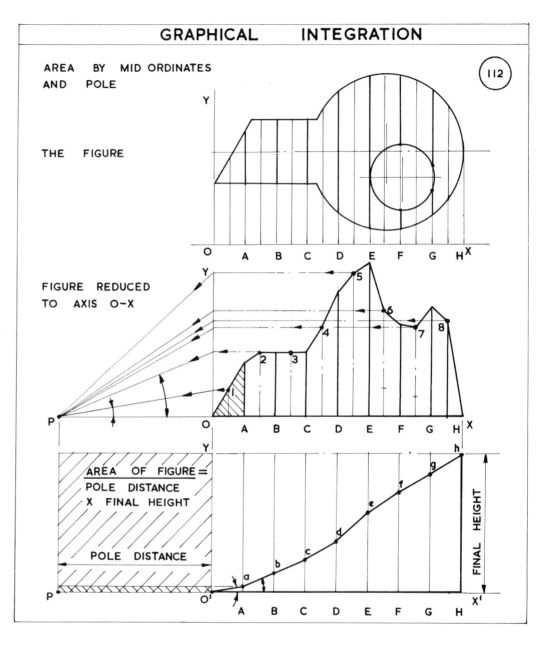

113. Simple Scales Where possible drawings should be drawn full size designated by the ratio 1:1. Where the object is large a smaller scale is adopted BS 308 1972 recommend divisors of 2, 5 and 10, giving ratios of 1:2; 1:5; 1:10; 1:20; 1:50; 1:100.

A. In this example, 25 mm are shown to represent 125 mm, giving a ratio of 1:5. This could also be designated by a representative fraction of 0·20. The method of drawing the scale is shown, note how the lefthand end shows small divisions of the unit beyond zero, this enables intermediate lengths such as 255 mm to be stepped off along the scale with the dividers—250 plus 5 beyond zero.

B. Where an object is small, a scale larger than full size can be used with advantage, enabling small details to be more easily drawn. The scale ratios suggested are 2:1; 5:1; 10:1; 20:1; 50:1; 100:1. In the example given, 100 mm represent 50 mm, using a ratio of 2:1; representational fraction of 2·0.

114. Diagonal Scales Greater accuracy on subdivisions of any scale may be obtained by the use of diagonal division (see No. 28).

C. In the example shown, a ratio of 2:1 shows 50 mm representing 25 mm with the use of diagonal lines intersecting parallel lines to give accurate subdivisions, depending on how finely the drawing is executed. Three typical measurements to scale are shown.

D. A further example of diagonal scale this time using a multiplier of 5.

EXERCISES
1. Draw a simple scale f.s. to read up to 100 mm by 1 mm.
2. Draw a diagonal scale 2:1, to read up to 75 mm by 0·5 mm.
3. Draw a diagonal scale 5:1, to read up to 15 mm by 0·5 mm.

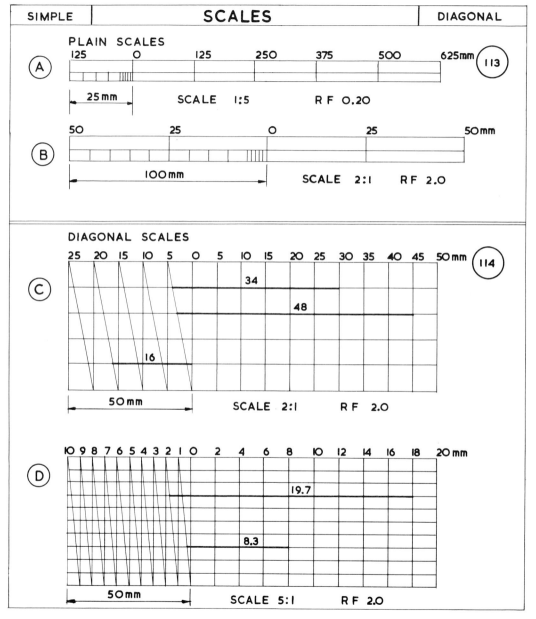

27

QUESTIONS ON PLANE GEOMETRY

Enlargement and Reduction of Plane Figures

1. Draw any suitable irregular hexagon, and by the pole method, reduce its area by one-fifth. (87)
2. Take the same hexagon, and by radials from an outside point, draw the figure twice the linear size. (89)
3. Draw a square of 75 mm side and reduce its area by one-twenty-fifth. (85)
4. Draw regular pentagon of 35 mm (21), and reduce this to a square of equal area. (36, 32)
5. Draw a circle which is equal in area to two other circles 35 mm and 50 mm in diameter. (83)
6. Draw a 50 mm square; draw a rectangle with a 55 mm base equal in area to the square, and draw a triangle having the same area but on a 70 mm base. (101, 34, 35)
7. Draw any scalene triangle, and draw a triangle of the same area on three-quarters of the same base.
8. Draw a quadrilateral and divide it into two equal areas by the method of 103.
9. Given perimeter 200 mm, base angle 37°, base 52 mm, draw the triangle. (102)
10. Given vertex angle 48°, altitude 35 mm, perimeter 155 mm, draw the triangle. (95)
11. Given base 5 cm, altitude 43 mm, perimeter 15 cm, draw the triangle. (110)
12. Given base 53 mm, opposite angle 40°, altitude 35 mm, draw the triangle. (108)
13. A square has a side of 4·5 cm. Increase its area in the ratio of 5:7. (111)

Circles

14. Three gears mesh whose radii are 50 mm, 70 mm and 80 mm. Draw the diagram of the three wheels when the pitch circle is 5 mm less than the gear size.
15. Draw three equal touching circles in a semicircle whose diameter is 100 mm.
16. Draw a circle to touch two lines meeting at an angle of 30°. The circle is to pass through a point which is 2 cm from one line, and 30 mm from the other. (66)
17. Draw a fully touching circle in a semicircle whose radius is 7 cm.
18. A triangle has sides 7 cm, 5 cm, 8·5 cm. Draw the inscribed and escribed circles.
19. Draw the interior and exterior common tangents to two circles diam. 36 mm and 54 mm with centres 74 mm apart. (45, 46)
20. A 50 mm diam. circle stands on a straight line. At 75 mm from the point of tangency at an angle of 45° is a point P. Draw a tangent to the circle and point. (46)
21. Draw a regular heptagon in a circle, diam. 70 mm. (41)
22. Find the diameter of a circle graphically whose perimeter is 12 cm. (104)
23. Find the perimeter when the diameter of a given circle is 50 mm. (105)

Loci

24. An arm 10 cm long, swings through 120°, being pivoted at one end. A point slides three-quarters of the distance along the arm during the swing. Draw the locus of a point (a) when the point moves from the pivot, (b) when the point moves from the outer end, (c) when the point moves to and from the inner end during its swing. (131)
25. A point moves so that it is always equidistant from the perimeters of two circles, 30 mm radius and 50 mm radius, whose centres are 100 mm apart. Plot the locus of the point.
26. In an angle of 60°, draw the locus of a point which is always twice the distance from one arm of the angle as it is from the other arm. Draw the locus for about 100 mm.
27. Draw the locus of a point on the perimeter of a 36 mm diam. circle which rolls (a) on a straight line for one revolution, (b) on the inside of a 150 mm diam. circle for one revolution.

Ellipse

28. Draw the ellipse when the two foci are 75 mm apart on a major axis whose length is 110 mm.
29. Draw a tangent and normal to above ellipse.
30. Draw a parabola whose focal point is 30 mm from the directrix.
31. Draw the rectangular hyperbola of a cone of 75 mm diam. base and altitude, the cut being 25 mm from the centre of the base. (122)
32. Draw the locus of a point which moves from zero to 25 mm along the normal of an ellipse during the time the normal moves round one-quarter of the ellipse. The ellipse has axes 75 mm and 110 mm.
33. Draw an ellipse of axes 6 cm and 10 cm by each of the three methods shown in 115, 117 and 118.
34. Show an ellipse as a section of a cylinder of 50 mm diam. cut at 30°. (119)
35. Draw a hyperbola of $\frac{5}{3}$ eccentricity whose focal point is 35 mm from the directrix.
36. Draw the hyperbola with a generating circle of 5 cm, and whose asymptotes are at 90°, with directrices 35 mm apart.
37. Draw the two hyperbolic curves shown in 126 and 127 with asymptotes at the angles shown and points located at twice the printed size.

Helices

38. Draw the helix of a point which moves to an altitude of 125 mm in one revolution along a cylinder 55 mm diam. (131)
39. Draw twice full size a diagrammatic vee thread of 60 mm diam. bolt, 10 mm pitch. (132)
40. Draw a lefthand thread, buttress type, 8 mm pitch, cut on a cylinder 75 mm diam., 75 mm long. (134)
41. Draw a righthand square thread 80 mm diam., lead 30 mm. (134)
42. Draw the spiral of a cone 60 mm diam. base and altitude. (136)
43. Draw an archimedean spiral whose initial and final vectors are 10 mm and 100 mm. (137)
44. Draw the spiral of a hemisphere of 90 mm diam. (136)
45. Draw the tangent and normal to the spiral of 43, when the vector angle is 120°. (144)

CONICS

Ellipse

Parabola

Hyperbola

Loci

Helices

Involutes

Cycloids

Gears

The Ellipse

115. The Ellipse 'The locus (path) of a point moving so that the sum of the distances from two fixed points (foci) is constant.' The Auxiliary Circle method employs a major and minor circle drawn on the two axes. Vertical and horizontal lines from the intersections of radial lines cutting the two circles give points through which the curve of the ellipse may be drawn.

116. Parts of the Ellipse The foci are found from the major and minor axes by describing half the major axis from the ends of the minor axis to cut the major axis. A normal is drawn by bisecting the angle formed when two foci are joined to a point on the ellipse. A tangent lies at right angles to the normal and passes through the point on the ellipse.

117. The Ellipse as the Plot of a Point The ellipse may be drawn as the locus of a point which moves so that its distances from a directrix (line) and a focal point are in a ratio less than unity. In the example shown, the ratio is as 3:4, i.e. 3 units are measured parallel to the directrix line, whilst 4 units are described from the focal point to intersect in a point on the ellipse.

118. The Ellipse may be drawn also by (*a*) *the Trammel*, in which the marking strip has half the major and minor axes marked on it and these points move along the two axes, the end of strip describing the ellipse; (*b*) the *Radial method*: points marked along the enclosing rectangle and major axis are intersected by radials giving points on the curve; (*c*) the *Cord method*, in which pins are driven into the focal points, and a loop of string is made allowing the pencil point to start drawing the curve at the end of the major axis.

119. The Ellipse as a Section of the Cone If a cone is cut by a plane passing through two opposite generators, the true face of the cut is an ellipse. Details of such projections are given in 161 and 164.

The ellipse may also be shown as a section of a cylinder.

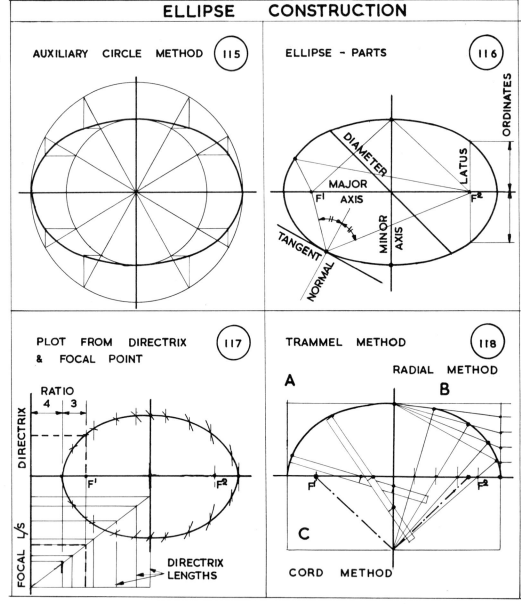

ELLIPSE CONSTRUCTION

AUXILIARY CIRCLE METHOD (115)

ELLIPSE – PARTS (116)

PLOT FROM DIRECTRIX & FOCAL POINT (117)

TRAMMEL METHOD (118)

CONICS

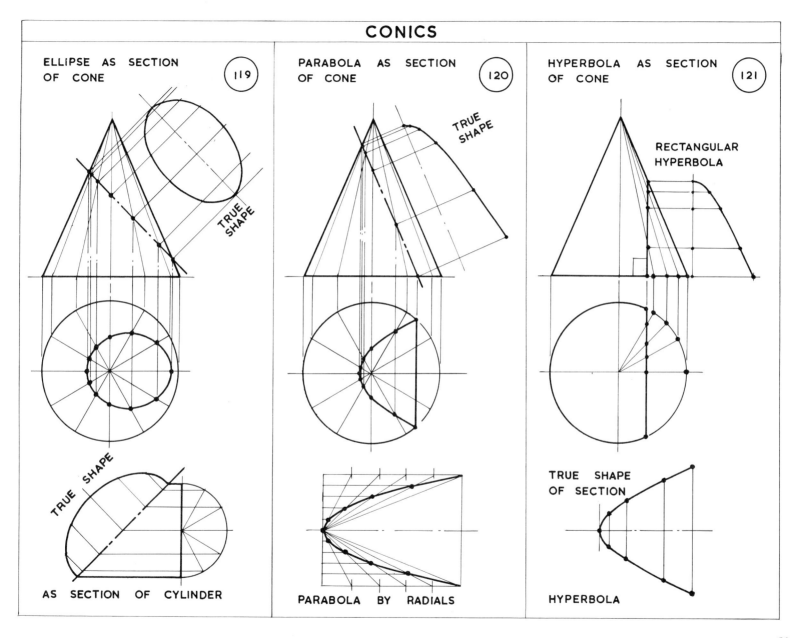

ELLIPSE AS SECTION OF CONE (119)

TRUE SHAPE

TRUE SHAPE

TRUE SHAPE AS SECTION OF CYLINDER

PARABOLA AS SECTION OF CONE (120)

TRUE SHAPE

PARABOLA BY RADIALS

HYPERBOLA AS SECTION OF CONE (121)

RECTANGULAR HYPERBOLA

TRUE SHAPE OF SECTION

HYPERBOLA

120. The Parabola as a Section of the Cone If a plane cuts a cone parallel to a generator, the true face of the section will be a parabola. The parabola may also be drawn by enclosing the space in a rectangle, and by parallels and radial intersectors points on the curve are found.

121. The Hyperbola as a Section of the Cone If a plane cuts a cone through a generator and the base at the same side of the axis, then the true face of the section is an hyperbola. If the plane is at right angles to the base, then a rectangular hyperbola results.

122. Conics The hyperbola, parabola and ellipse are shown as the loci of a point which moves in fixed ratios to a directrix (line) and a focal point.

The Ratio is : $\dfrac{\text{distance from focus}}{\text{distance from directrix}}$.

The ratio for the hyperbola is greater than unity e.g. 4/3;
The ratio for the parabola is unity, 1/1;
The ratio for the ellipse is less than unity, e.g. 3/4;

The above conics may be constructed by drawing first the line of the directrix, then the focal point on a line perpendicular to the directrix. A simple graph gives progressive distances in the ratio required in the diagrams. The distances are drawn as parallels to the directrix and as arcs radiating from the focal point. The intersections give points along the required curve.

Draw the curve when the focal point is 70 mm from the directrix.

123. Parabola The parabola is shown as the locus of a point which moves at a constant distance from both the directrix and the focal point; this ratio is unity. Draw the curve when the focal point is 40 mm from the directrix.

124. Hyperbola The hyperbola is shown as the locus of a point which moves at a constant ratio of eccentricity greater than unity. The diagram shows the curve when the ratio is 4/3. Draw the curve when the focal point is 70 mm from the directrix.

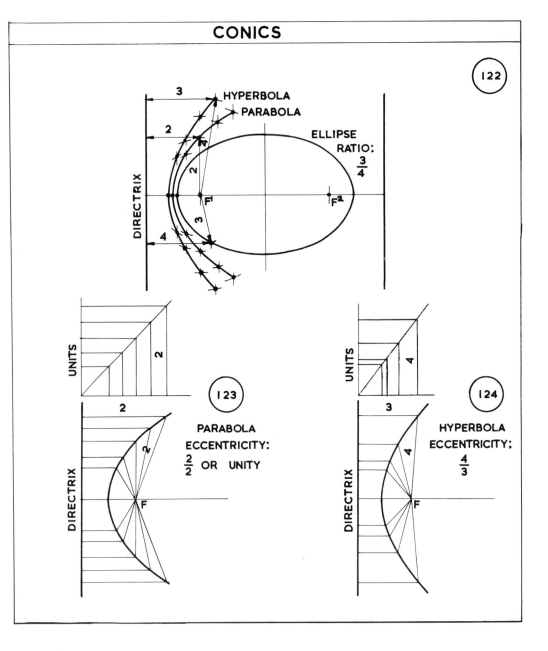

CONICS

125. The Hyperbola The parts of the hyperbola and its construction are shown in detail.

Draw first the transverse axis and the conjugate axis at rightangles. Draw the two directrices. Fix the two focal points on the transverse axis. Fix the vertices by applying the ratio of eccentricity. Draw the auxiliary circle.

Draw the asymptotes through the intersection of the directrix and the auxiliary circle. Plot the points through which the curve is drawn by first fixing any convenient points A, A′, A², A³, on the transverse axis, and then describing arcs from the two focal points with the radii as shown in the diagram: V A from F′; V′A from F², etc. Draw the curve through the points.

Notice how the tangent is on the bisector of the angle made by joining a point on the curve to the two foci. The normal is at right angles to the tangent.

126. Given Asymptote and point on Curve When only the asymptotes and a point on the curve are given, the curve points may be plotted by drawing parallels and radials to the asymptotes and from O respectively.

127. Rectangular Hyperbola Given the asymptotes and a point on the hyperbolic curve, draw parallels to the asymptotes; radials from O. Draw the curve through the intersections as shown in the diagram.

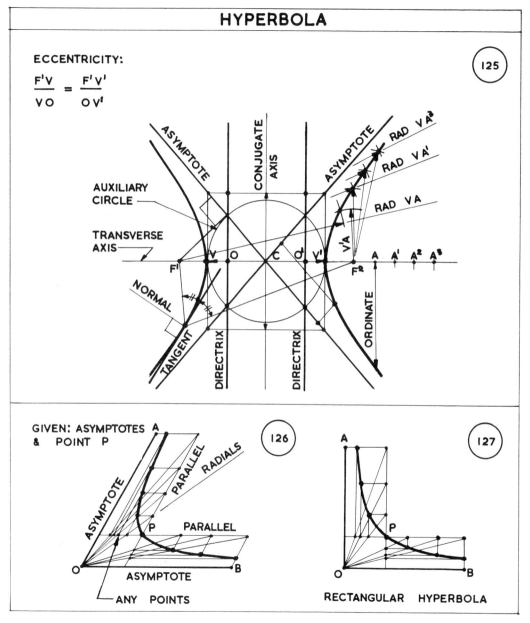

HYPERBOLA

ECCENTRICITY:

$$\frac{F'V}{VO} = \frac{F'V'}{OV'}$$

GIVEN: ASYMPTOTES & POINT P

RECTANGULAR HYPERBOLA

128. A. **Straight Line Locus of P** The path of a moving point is its locus. In this diagram the point moves at a fixed perpendicular distance from a straight line, and gives a further straight line as the locus.

B. The second diagram shows the locus of a point moving at a fixed distance from zig-zag profile; it yields a similar contour to the locus.

C. When a point moves at a fixed distance from another point, the locus is a circle.

D. The diagram shows the locus of a point moving at a fixed distance from a triangle. Notice how the arc at the vertices has the given distance as its radius.

129. E. The locus of a point C following a contour at a fixed distance. Plotting involves the use of circles, straight lines and radii.

130. F. a cam and follower are given, a single revolution performance graph is shown in the diagram. Twelve points on the cam are taken, rotated to the height line, and projected to the graph where the performance terms of closed, lift, dwell (open), fall (closing), closed, are self-explanatory.

Cams of various profiles are used for the continuous control of poppet valves in i.c. engines, printing machines etc., where repeated motions are required. If the cam turns at a given speed, the time of the sequence of rise and fall can be calculated in relation to degrees of angle through which the cam turns.

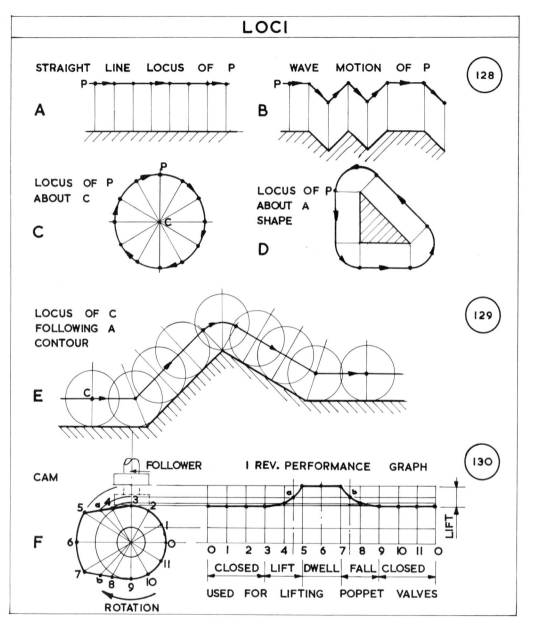

131. Helices Righthand Helix. 'The locus of a point moving at a constant speed radially and axially.'

Draw the elevation of the cylinder, draw the generators 0–11 (twelve); divide the lead distance (representing one revolution), into the same number of divisions (12). Plot the points of the helix by intersections of the generators and lead divisions. Draw the helical curve through the points.

Notice that a righthand helix rises to the righthand, and a lefthand helix rises to the lefthand.

132. Righthand Vee Thread A screw thread of 60° vee form requires two helices to be drawn, one for the external diameter and one for the root diameter. Both use the same lead divisions, but have different generators. The diagram should make the method clear. Draw the bolt shown with major diameter of 6 cm, and a lead of 1 cm.

133. Various Helices Five helices are shown plotted on the same cylinder. at A′, A, B, C, righthand helices are drawn; D is a lefthand helix. The quick helix of D is similar to that of the volutes in drills and reamers.

134. Square Righthand Thread A section of the thread form is a square, two helices are required, one for the major external diameter, and a lesser one for the root diameter. Draw the screw thread shown, major diameter 75 mm, lead 24 mm.

EXERCISES
1. A cylinder is 50 mm in diameter and 80 mm in length. A point moves in a lefthand rotation along the cylinder making one revolution in the length. Plot the locus.
2. Another point moves in a righthand rotation, and makes two revolutions along the cylinder, plot the locus.
3. A metric bolt has a diameter of 10 mm and a thread pitch of 1·5 mm. Draw as a simple vee thread, 6 × F.S.

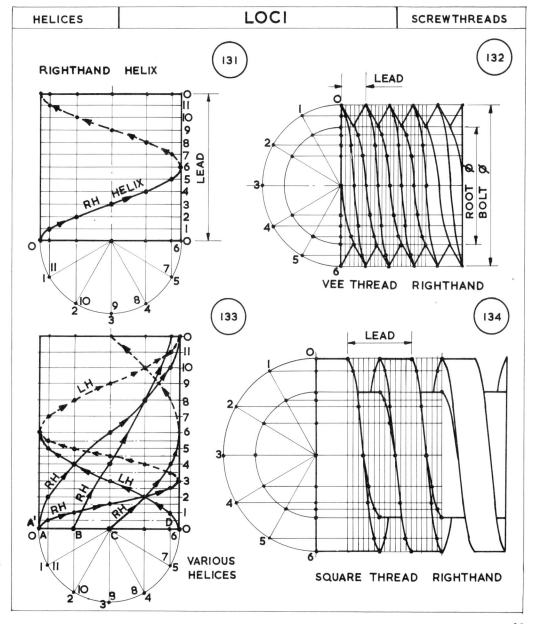

RIGHTHAND HELIX

RH HELIX

VEE THREAD   RIGHTHAND

VARIOUS HELICES

SQUARE THREAD   RIGHTHAND

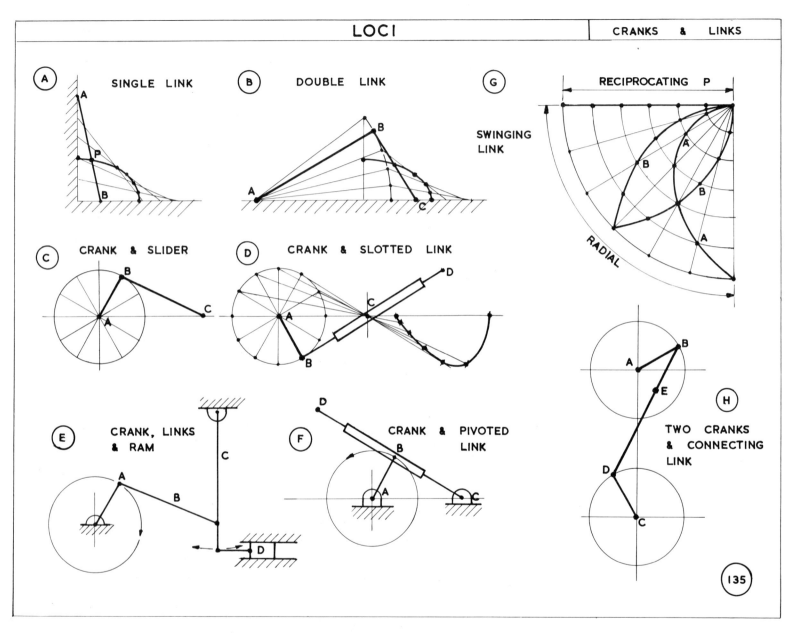

A — SINGLE LINK

B — DOUBLE LINK

G — SWINGING LINK — RECIPROCATING P — RADIAL

C — CRANK & SLIDER

D — CRANK & SLOTTED LINK

E — CRANK, LINKS & RAM

F — CRANK & PIVOTED LINK

H — TWO CRANKS & CONNECTING LINK

135

135. Cranks and Links

A. **Single Link** A bar or link AB lies with its ends in contact with two surfaces, and slides as shown. Plot the locus of point P on the link.

B. **Double Link** Two links, AB, BC, pinjointed.

C. **Crank and Slider** A crank AB rotates about A, BC is a link, C sliding to and fro along a horizontal surface.

D. **Crank and Slotted Link** AB is a crank, BD is a slotted link allowing movement (restricted) about C. Plot the locus of D.

E. **Crank, Links and Ram** Draw the motion when the crank is 40 mm long.

F. **Crank and Pivoted Link** Draw the motion with the crank length 40 mm, plot the locus of D.

G. **Swinging Link** A link swings through 90° pivoted at one end. A point P moves along the link as the link rotates.

H. **Two Cranks and Connecting Link**

136. Conical Spiral
The locus of a point which traces a circular path on the surface of a cone from a point on the base to the apex.

137. Archimedean Spiral
This spiral may be stated to have an 'initial vector', and a 'final vector', and may make one or more revolutions as required.

138. Involute of a Square

139. Involute of a Circle
Draw the initial circle or generating circle. Divide into twelve parts by setsquare. Draw a tangent to the circle at point 0, and mark off twelve divisions each equal to one-twelfth of the circumference of the initial circle, by calculation, or use method in 107. Draw tangents from points of the circle 1 to 11, cut off the lengths of the tangents equal to its arc from 0. Draw the involute curve through the points as in the diagram. See 140 for its application to the involute gear tooth.

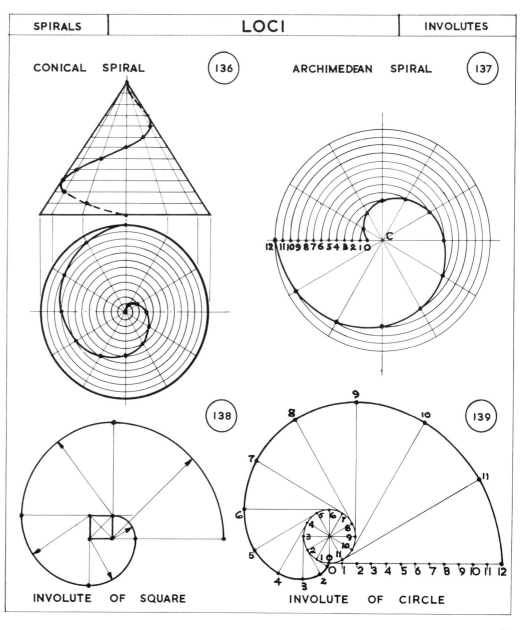

CONICAL SPIRAL (136) ARCHIMEDEAN SPIRAL (137)

(138) (139)

INVOLUTE OF SQUARE INVOLUTE OF CIRCLE

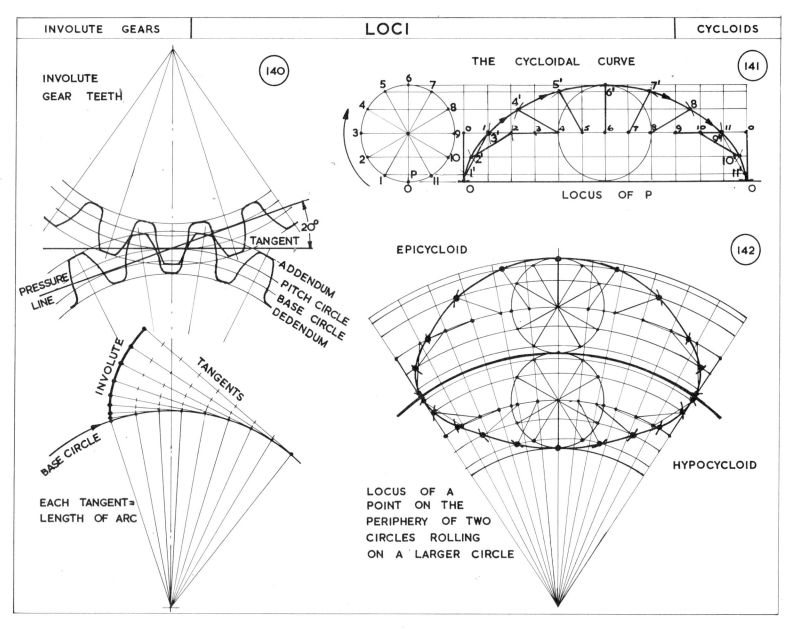

140 INVOLUTE GEAR TEETH

20°

TANGENT

PRESSURE LINE

ADDENDUM
PITCH CIRCLE
BASE CIRCLE
DEDENDUM

INVOLUTE

TANGENTS

BASE CIRCLE

EACH TANGENT = LENGTH OF ARC

141 THE CYCLOIDAL CURVE

LOCUS OF P

142 EPICYCLOID

HYPOCYCLOID

LOCUS OF A POINT ON THE PERIPHERY OF TWO CIRCLES ROLLING ON A LARGER CIRCLE

140. Involute Gear Teeth The method of drawing the involute curve has been shown in 139, and its application is shown in more detail in this diagram. The pitch circle is the meshing circle of two gears. The base circle is the generating circle for the involute curve which gives the profile of the gear teeth; it is tangential to the pressure line of 20°.

141. Cycloidal Curve The locus of a point on the periphery of a circle which rolls without slipping on a straight line. Draw the circle and the straight line. Draw its twelve divisions by setsquare. Draw the rectangular projection, height as the diameter of the circle, length as the circumference. Mark the twelve divisions, representing the centre of the circle as it moves. Plot the locus of point P, imagine the radial line as a spoke in the turning wheel.

142. Epicycloid and Hypocycloid The locus of a point on the periphery of (*a*) a circle rolling outside a larger circle, (*b*) rolling round the inside of a larger circle, as shown in the diagram.

EXERCISES
1. Draw the cycloidal curve of a circle 50 mm diam.
2. Draw the epicycloidal curve of a 50 mm diam. circle rolling outside a circle of 80 mm diam.
3. Draw the hypocycloidal curve using similar circles.

143. Simple Gear Train A simple train of gears may be to reduce speed or gain greater effort, or to fix a relationship between two shafts.

Bevel Gears Enables two shafts to be driven whose axes may not be in the same plane. Equal bevels are shown, but a reduction may be effected by unequal bevel gears.

Worm Gearing A helical worm turning a toothed wormwheel, giving a large reduction. One turn of the worm moves the wheel one tooth, but multistart worms are used also.

Simple Gear Box By means of splined shafts, gears may be moved laterally along the shaft to disengage the drive. Double reductions may be effected in small space using shafts with parallel axes.

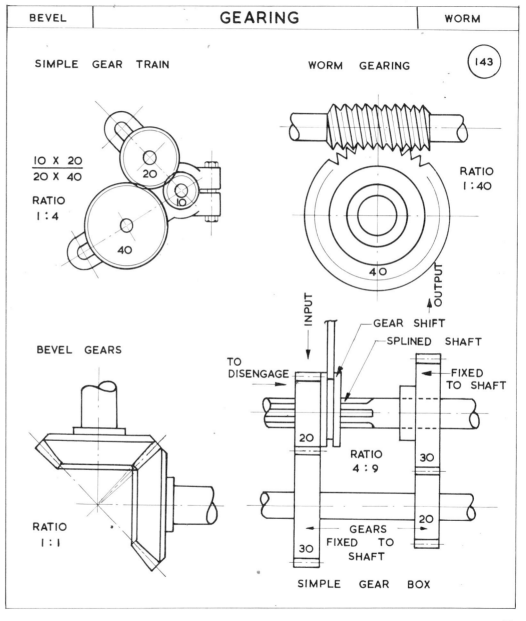

SIMPLE GEAR TRAIN

$$\frac{10 \times 20}{20 \times 40}$$

RATIO 1 : 4

20

10

40

WORM GEARING

RATIO 1 : 40

40

BEVEL GEARS

RATIO 1 : 1

INPUT

OUTPUT

TO DISENGAGE

GEAR SHIFT

SPLINED SHAFT

FIXED TO SHAFT

20

RATIO 4 : 9

30

30

20

GEARS FIXED TO SHAFT

SIMPLE GEAR BOX

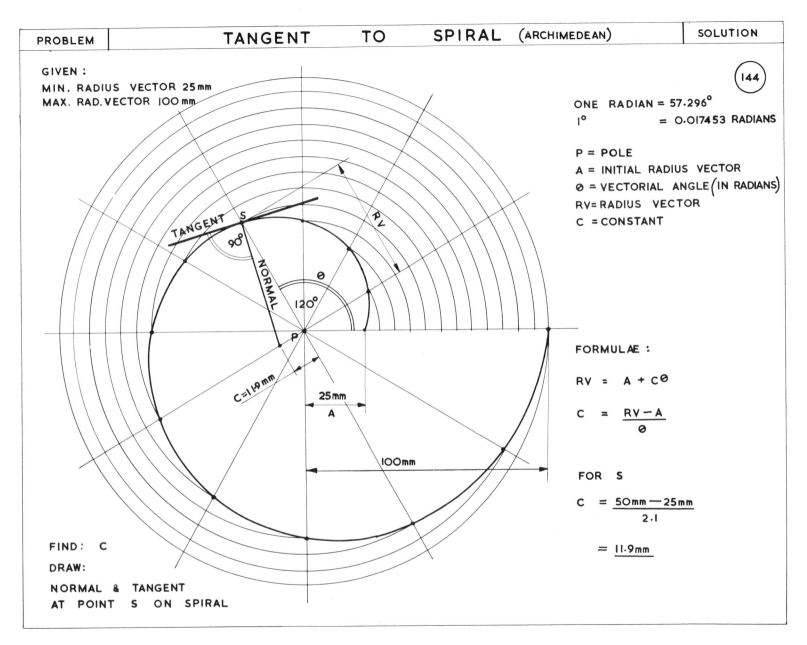

GIVEN :
MIN. RADIUS VECTOR 25 mm
MAX. RAD. VECTOR 100 mm

144

ONE RADIAN = 57.296°
1° = 0.017453 RADIANS

P = POLE
A = INITIAL RADIUS VECTOR
θ = VECTORIAL ANGLE (IN RADIANS)
RV = RADIUS VECTOR
C = CONSTANT

TANGENT S

90°

NORMAL

120°

RV

θ

C = 11·9 mm

25 mm
A

100 mm

FORMULAE :

$RV = A + C\theta$

$C = \dfrac{RV - A}{\theta}$

FOR S

$C = \dfrac{50mm - 25mm}{2·1}$

$= \underline{11·9 mm}$

FIND: C

DRAW:

NORMAL & TANGENT
AT POINT S ON SPIRAL

144. Tangent to Archimedean Spiral The diagram shows the method of drawing a normal and tangent to the above curve. Given the minimum and maximum vectors draw the spiral, see 137. Fix point S on the radius vector at 120°. Before the normal and tangent to the curve at S can be drawn, the value of C, which is a constant, must be found. Apply the formula shown in the diagram, where θ, the vectorial angle of S, is stated in radians. In this case, since the angle is 120°, the radian value will be $120 \times 0.017453 = 2.1$, giving finally the value of C as 11.9 mm.

EXERCISES

1. Given the final and initial vector lengths as 60 mm and 10 mm respectively, draw an Archimedean spiral having $1\frac{1}{2}$ revolutions (make 12 radial divisions, and 18 vector divisions).
2. Draw the involute of a triangle of 30 mm side, for 6 arcs.
3. Draw the involute curve whose generating circle is 40 mm diam.

145. A. (*a*) The small circle rolls once inside the larger circle, whose diameter is 80 mm. Plot the locus of P. What is the name of the locus? (*b*) A square rolls inside the circle shown in (*a*), plot the locus of P_1. The square has a 35 mm side.
B. A circle of 30 mm diam. rolls outside a quarter-ellipse, major axis 130 mm, minor axis 80 mm. Plot the locus of P.
C. Draw the spiral of the hemisphere shown, 50 mm radius.
D. Draw righthand helix on the cylinder shown beginning at H^1. Draw also a lefthand helix beginning at H^2.
E. Draw the motion shown in the diagram full size, plot the locus of P^1; state the travel of P.
F. The diagram shows part of the drawing of a hyperbola, with P a point on the curve. Draw the hyperbola. (See 125.)

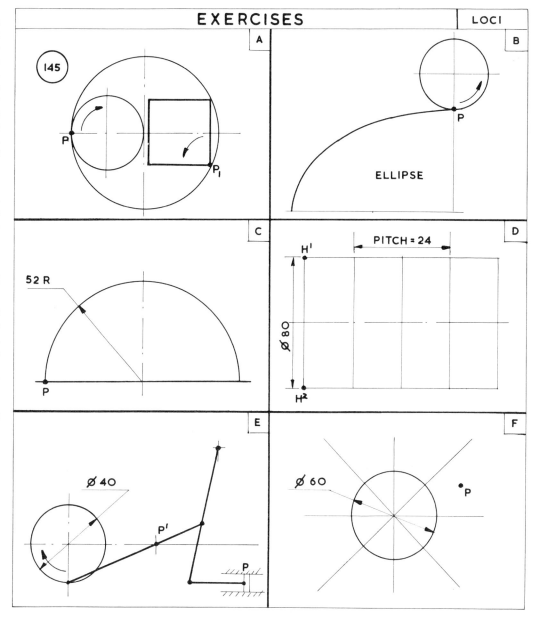

EXERCISES — LOCI

ELLIPSE

52 R

PITCH = 24

⌀ 80

H¹ H²

⌀ 40

⌀ 60

41

146. A. Calculate the area of the figure shown by the method shown in 112.

B. The diagram shows a cone cut by three planes. Draw the section on A A, name it; indicate its two axes; show a second method of drawing its shape given these two axes.

 Project the section on B B, name it. Draw the rectangle enclosing the shape, and show another method of drawing the shape.

 Project the shape on the section C C, name it. Show an alternative method of drawing the shape given its enclosing rectangle.

C. Two radial cams are shown. Draw each, and project the performance graph of each. State the details of the performance, if the cams turn at one revolution per half minute.

D. Draw the diagram twice full size. The circle rolls clockwise along the contour. Draw the locus of point P.

E. A cylinder of 50 mm diam. is cut by a plane 30° to its axis, draw the section and state the name of the shape.

F. Draw an ellipse, major axis 120 mm, minor axis 60 mm using (*a*) the cord and pin method, (*b*) auxiliary circle method, (*c*) the trammel.

G. Draw a cam to give 10 mm lift from a basic circle of 50 mm diam. The performance should show 90° closed, 90° rise, 90° dwell, 90° fall.

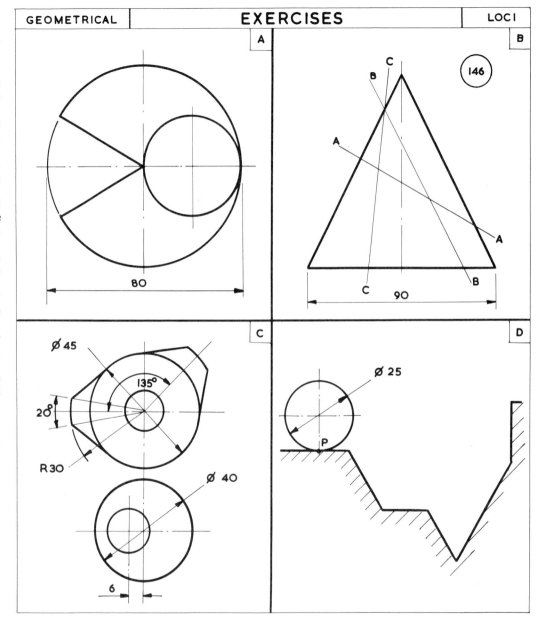

ORTHOGRAPHIC PROJECTION

First Angle

Third Angle

Sections

Auxiliary Planes

147. Orthographic Projection In the first angle projection of plans to the horizontal plane and elevations to the vertical plane(s) the object is visualised as being inside a box whose walls and floor are the planes on to which the various views are projected. The diagram should help to make this clear.

Third angle projection is also much used; this is discussed in 150.

148. Shaped Block in First Angle The diagram shows how orthographic projection will appear when the planes are opened out from the box form in 147. The vertical planes, A, B, C, are in the upper portion, and have the elevations projected on them. Below the X Y line is the horizontal plane, on to which the plan has been projected.

To begin the drawing, the overall sizes of the object should be calculated, spaced well on the paper and the X Y line drawn. The plan is usually drawn first, and the front elevation projected upwards to the vertical plane. Often the nature of the object may deem it necessary to draw the elevation first, or to draw details partly in both as the drawing proceeds. Sometimes a centre line in the plan or elevation is the starting point; often, end elevations have to be drawn as part of the early drawing enabling details to be projected in other views.

Drawings can be full size or to a stated scale. Accuracy of dimension and detail are primary essentials, since mistakes can be costly in production. Pictorial views are shown of the block in 229.

Note first angle symbol which may be used instead of words.

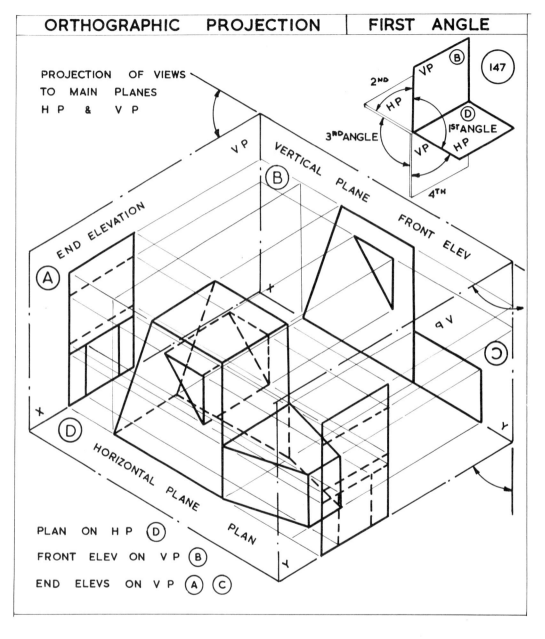

ORTHOGRAPHIC PROJECTION | FIRST ANGLE

PROJECTION OF VIEWS TO MAIN PLANES HP & VP

PLAN ON HP Ⓓ
FRONT ELEV ON VP Ⓑ
END ELEVS ON VP Ⓐ Ⓒ

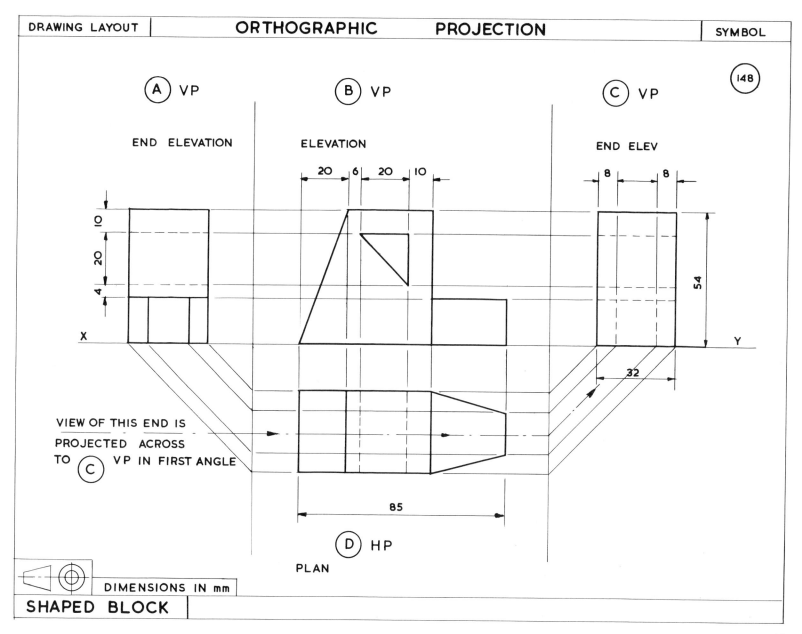

(A) VP

(B) VP

(C) VP

END ELEVATION

ELEVATION

END ELEV

20   6   20   10

8   8

10

20

4

54

X

Y

32

VIEW OF THIS END IS
PROJECTED ACROSS
TO (C) VP IN FIRST ANGLE

85

(D) HP

PLAN

DIMENSIONS IN mm

SHAPED BLOCK

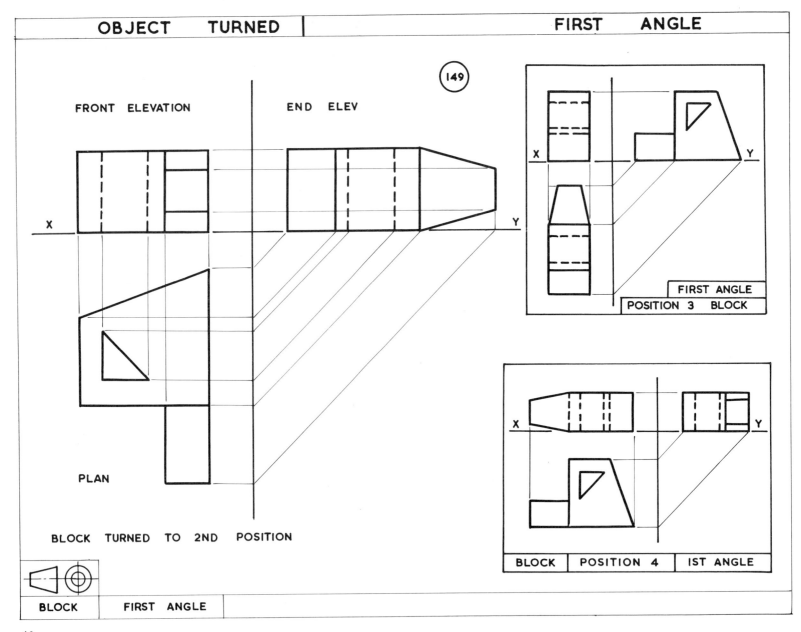

FRONT ELEVATION   END ELEV

149

X   Y

PLAN

BLOCK   TURNED   TO   2ND   POSITION

FIRST ANGLE
POSITION 3   BLOCK

BLOCK   POSITION 4   1ST ANGLE

BLOCK   FIRST ANGLE

149. Object Turned to Second Position Examination questions often require a given view such as an elevation, to be drawn as the plan in a further drawing. The given view should then be drawn first on the new plane, and other views projected from it.

Notice that in first angle, an end elevation is the view of the opposite end of the object, the view being projected across the front elevation.

The diagrams show the shaped block turned to three further positions from that in 148.

150. Third Angle Projection Much American and Continental technical and engineering drawing uses the third-angle method of projection. In this projection the object is placed in the third angle shown in the small sketch, and the plan and elevations projected on to the planes which are visualised as being transparent, the object being viewed through them. When the planes forming the transparent box are opened out, the plan appears *above* the front elevation, whilst the end elevations are diagrams of the ends *nearest* to the plane and *not* of the opposite end as in first angle (see 147).

Examiners now require a knowledge of both methods, questions sometimes being set in one angle and requiring a solution in the other angle of projection. The exercises appearing later in the book are set using both angles, so care must be taken to read the headings of the diagrams on every page to see whether the views are in first or third angle of projection.

Note third angle symbol which may be used instead of words.

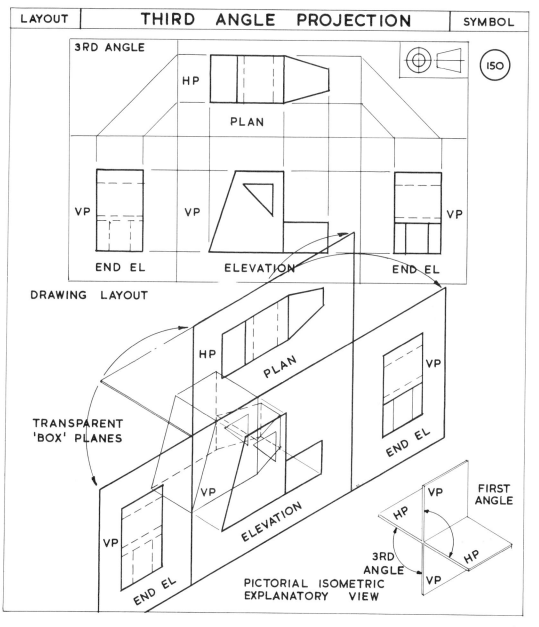

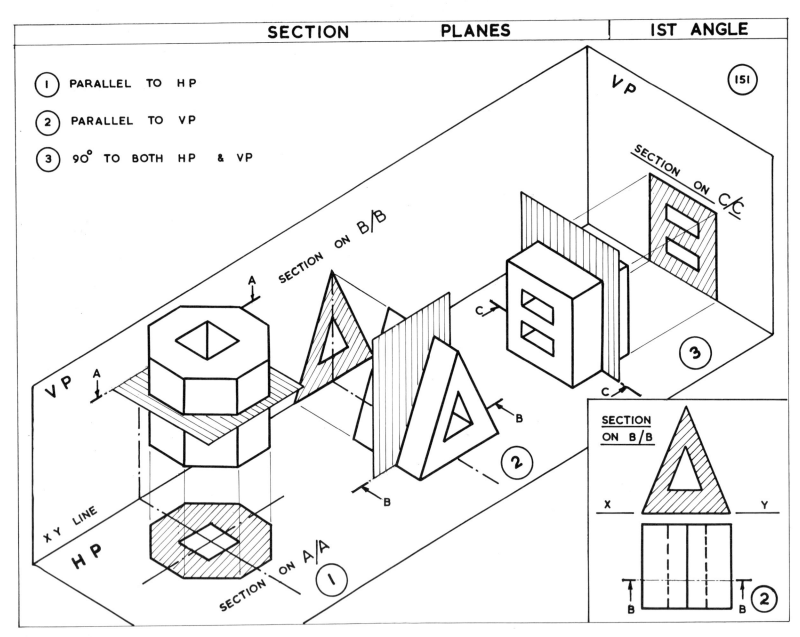

PARALLEL   TO   H P

PARALLEL   TO   V P

90° TO BOTH   H P & V P

151

VP

SECTION ON C/C

SECTION ON B/B

VP

HP

X Y LINE

SECTION ON A/A

SECTION ON B/B

X ──────── Y

151. Section Planes The ordinary views so far discussed may not show inner details of the object and cutting planes are used to obtain hidden forms. They are 'sections' or 'sectional views'. The three usual planes are shown at 1, 2 and 3 in the diagram. No. 1 is the horizontal plane which gives sections in the plan. No. 2 gives sections in the front elevation. No. 3 gives sections in the end elevation.

Note particularly the lettered sectional plane indicator line A A, B B, C C; the arrowheads show where the section is to be projected.

When a section is drawn, note that the front portion of the object is considered removed, and the cut face of what is left is the section. Note that these planes are parallel to either the main horizontal plane or the vertical planes. Angled planes are dealt with in 157.

152. Sections, First Angle An hexagonal prism is shown cut by a vertical section plane which is parallel to the main vertical plane. The pictorial view should help in understanding the problem. The lower diagram shows the first angle projections.

153. Sections, First Angle A vertical section plane cuts an hexagonal pyramid parallel to the main vertical plane. The first angle projections are shown in the lower diagram.

The drawings should be made twice the printed size.

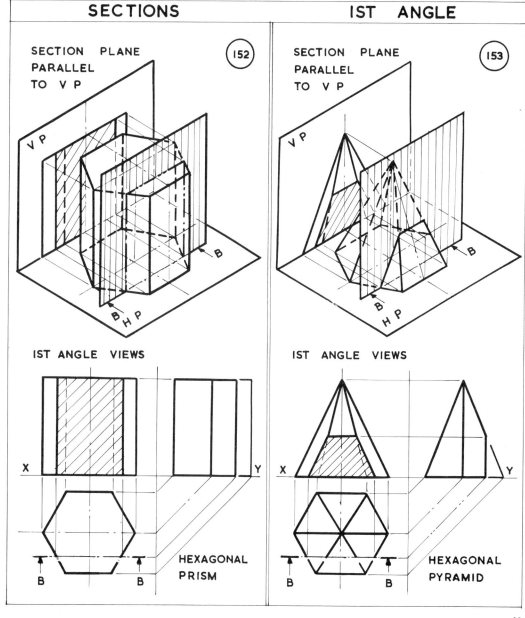

SECTIONS   IST ANGLE

SECTION PLANE PARALLEL TO V P (152)

SECTION PLANE PARALLEL TO V P (153)

IST ANGLE VIEWS

IST ANGLE VIEWS

HEXAGONAL PRISM

HEXAGONAL PYRAMID

154. Sections, Third Angle The pictorial view shows a cylinder cut by a plane parallel to the main horizontal plane. The third angle projections are shown in the lower diagram: note the plan above the elevation.

155. Sections, Third Angle The pictorial view shows a right circular cone cut by a plane parallel to the main vertical plane. The third angle projections of the cone are shown, note the section indicator line CC.

Note that when the section plane is parallel to a main projection plane, the face of the section projected is the true shape. In 151–155 the sections appear as sectional plans or elevations. Later, angled section planes are discussed (157).

The drawings should be made twice the printed size.

Objects shown in 169, 203, 247–251 are suitable for sectioning, and both first and third angle projections should be used alternately to obtain maximum practice. Always state the angle of projection used.

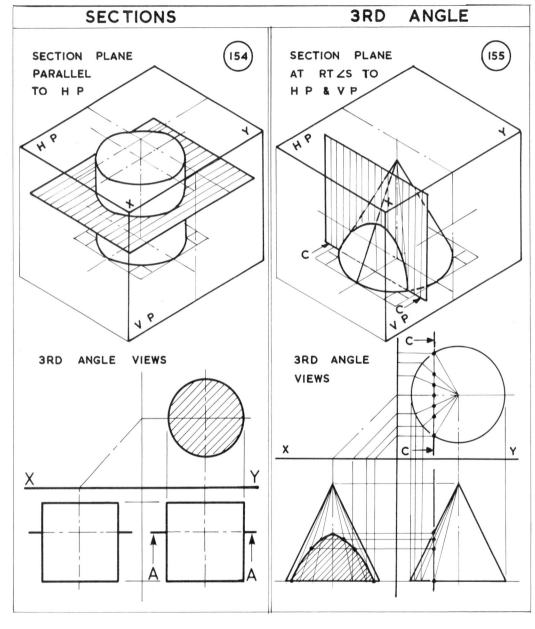

SECTIONS   3RD ANGLE

SECTION PLANE PARALLEL TO H P   (154)

SECTION PLANE AT RT ∠S TO H P & V P   (155)

3RD ANGLE VIEWS

3RD ANGLE VIEWS

156. Exercises in Sectioning

A. An hexagonal pyramid is shown in first angle, to be sectioned by a horizontal plane. Draw the projections in (*a*) first angle, (*b*) in third angle.

B. A 75 mm diam. sphere is sectioned by a horizontal plane. Draw the projections in both first and third angle projections.

C. A pierced, shaped prism is angled to the vertical plane, and is sectioned as shown, the projection being in third angle. Draw the views shown, plus an end elevation showing the section face.

D. First angle projections of a shaped block are given. Draw the views, and an end elevation giving the section.

E. Views of a circular cam are given in third angle, draw the views and a sectional view as indicated.

F. A turned solid is shown in third angle projection, draw the views and the sectional view required.

Other objects suitable for simple sectioning and projection are given in 169, 203, 247–251.

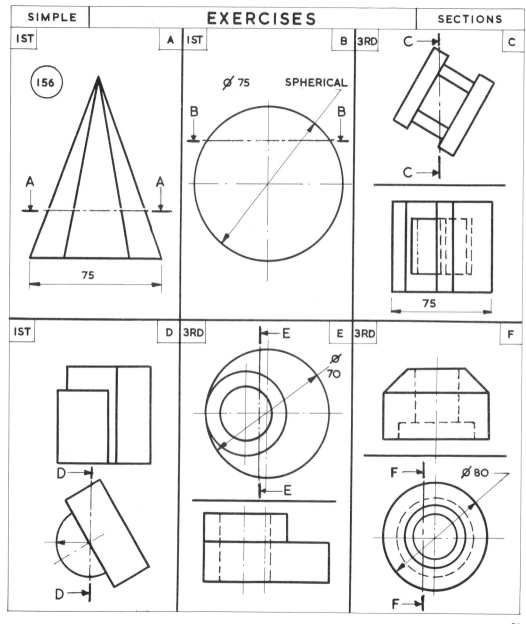

51

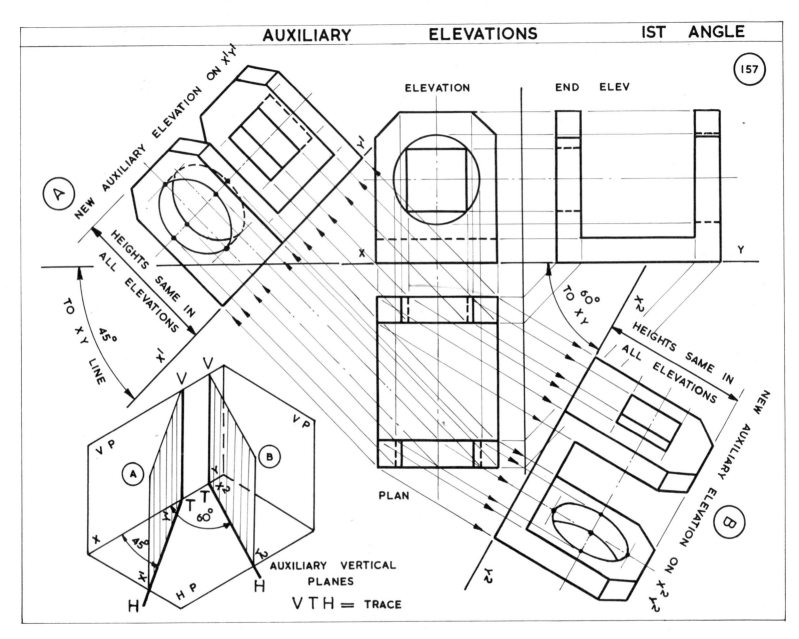

157

A

NEW AUXILIARY ELEVATION ON x¹y¹

HEIGHTS SAME IN
ALL ELEVATIONS

TO x y LINE

45°

x¹

ELEVATION

END ELEV

Y

60°
TO x y

x₂

HEIGHTS SAME IN
ALL ELEVATIONS

NEW AUXILIARY ELEVATION ON x₂y₂

B

y₂

PLAN

VP

VP

A

B

VP

x¹

T T
45° 60°

x

x₂

y₂

HP

H

H

AUXILIARY VERTICAL
PLANES

V T H = TRACE

AUXILIARY ELEVATIONS AND PLANS

157. Auxiliary Elevations Additional or auxiliary vertical projection planes are sometimes required, on to which an auxiliary elevation may be projected to show special details of an object. The auxiliary plane is indicated by its traces V T H in the diagram.

As in the ordinary elevations, they are also projected from the plan. The new angle will be stated, usually at so many degrees to the original X Y line. The new elevation is projected normal (i.e. at right angles) to this line X′Y′, *heights remaining unchanged* as in the other elevations, such heights being stepped off by the dividers on the lines from points projected from the plan.

Two auxiliary elevations are shown in the diagram, and should make the method clear. Note that circles may become ellipses, rectangles foreshortened.

Auxiliary views are generally used to show true shapes of sections and objects which are not shown projected on the main horizontal and vertical planes, details appear on the next pages.

158. Auxiliary Plans The method is similar to that above, a new X′Y′ line is stated at an angle to the original X Y line, or the traces of the new plane may be given V T H. The new plan is then projected from the elevation as shown; this time the *widths* below the X Y lines *remain unchanged*, and are stepped off by dividers along the projected lines. Because of lack of space, the diagram shows the new plan too close to the original plan; normally auxiliary views should be projected well clear of other views.

Notice again how circles become ellipses, and rectangles become foreshortened.

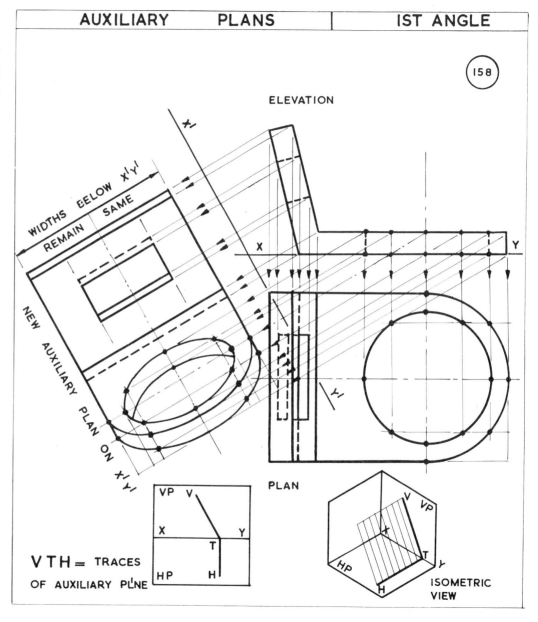

ELEVATION

WIDTHS BELOW X′Y′ REMAIN SAME

NEW AUXILIARY PLAN ON X′Y′

PLAN

ISOMETRIC VIEW

V T H = TRACES OF AUXILIARY PLANE

53

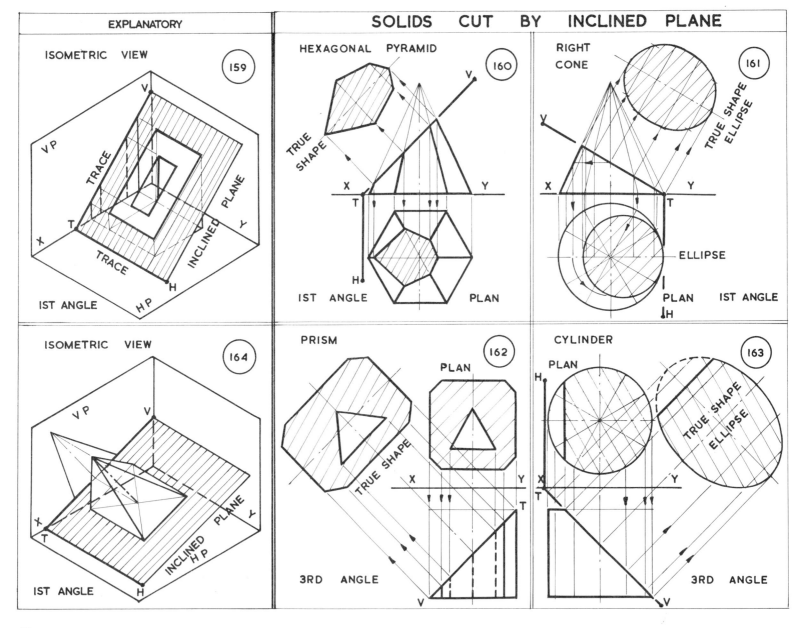

ISOMETRIC VIEW (159)

VP

TRACE

TRACE

INCLINED PLANE

V

T

X

Y

H

HP

1ST ANGLE

HEXAGONAL PYRAMID (160)

V

TRUE SHAPE

X Y

T

H

1ST ANGLE PLAN

RIGHT CONE (161)

TRUE SHAPE ELLIPSE

Y

X Y

T

ELLIPSE

PLAN 1ST ANGLE

H

ISOMETRIC VIEW (164)

VP

V

INCLINED HP

X

T

Y

H

1ST ANGLE

PRISM (162)

PLAN

TRUE SHAPE

X Y

T

V

3RD ANGLE

CYLINDER (163)

PLAN

H

TRUE SHAPE ELLIPSE

X Y

T

V

3RD ANGLE

159. Solids Cut by the Inclined Plane Objects may also be represented as being cut by the auxiliary plane inclined to either the main horizontal plane or to the main vertical plane. The pictorial view shows a hollow square prism cut by an auxiliary plane inclined to the main horizontal plane. The traces of the plane are V T H. The plan and elevation should be drawn as an exercise, and the true shape projected as in the next diagram. First angle.

160. Hexagonal Pyramid Cut by an Inclined Plane, traces as V T H. The plan and elevation should be drawn, the cutting plane fixed by V T H, and the points of the section projected back to the plan. The section given in the plan is not the true shape, and an auxiliary plan is projected from the elevation, widths being unchanged from the original plan.

161. Right Cone Cut by plane inclined to H.P. Draw the plan and elevation of the cone, draw the traces V T H of the inclined plane cutting the cone. Draw the twelve generators of the cone in plan, project these to the base line in the elevation; join to the apex. Project the points on the generators where the plane cuts each to the plan, and draw the ellipse in the plan. Project a new auxiliary plan parallel to V T, and take the widths of the ordinates from the original plan. This second ellipse is the true shape of the section. First angle.

162. Prism Cut by Inclined Plane Third angle projections of a shaped prism are given, cut by an inclined plane V T. An auxiliary plan has been projected giving the true shape of the section.

163. Cylinder Cut by Inclined Plane Third angle projections of a cylinder cut by an inclined plane HTV are given. Draw twice the printed size.

164. Solids Standing on the Inclined Plane Objects may also be represented as standing on the inclined plane.

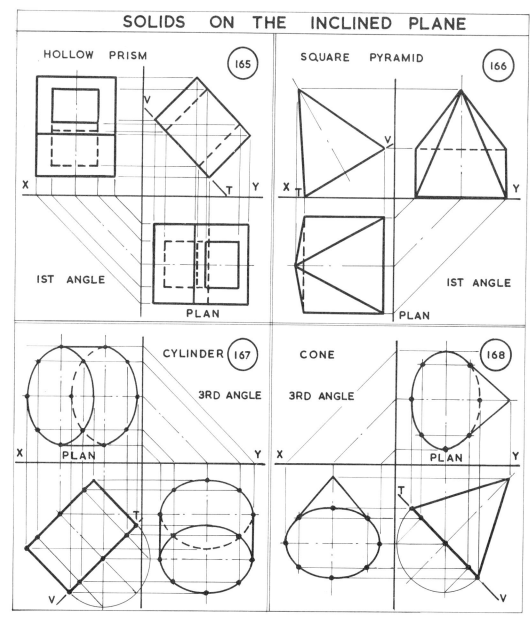

SOLIDS ON THE INCLINED PLANE

HOLLOW PRISM 165

SQUARE PYRAMID 166

1ST ANGLE

PLAN

1ST ANGLE

PLAN

CYLINDER 167

3RD ANGLE

PLAN

CONE 168

3RD ANGLE

PLAN

55

165. Hollow Prism standing on the inclined plane
First angle projections of the prism are shown.
Draw the elevation first, project the plan. The end
elevation can now be drawn.

166. Square Pyramid standing on an inclined plane
VT Draw the elevation first, project the plan and
project the end elevation.

167. Cylinder standing on an inclined plane VT
Eight points on the circle should be obtained by
enclosing the cylinder circle in a square plus its
diagonals giving eight intersection points for
projection. (See 168.) Third angle.

168. Cone standing on an inclined plane TV Draw
the elevation first, project the plan, the eight projection points are given in the construction semicircle shown, enabling the ellipses to be projected.

EXERCISES

169. A. First angle projections of an hexagonal
pyramid cut by an inclined plane VTH. Draw
the projections and project the true shape of
the section.
B. A right cone is cut by a plane as shown. The
cone is pierced by a cylindrical hole. Draw a
plan and two elevations. First angle.
C. Third angle views of a bearing block are given,
cut by a plane whose traces are HTV. Draw
the two views; project an auxiliary view showing the true shape of the section.
D. First angle views of a right cone are given, cut
by an inclined plane, VTH; project the true
shape of the section.
E. Third angle views of a circular eccentric are
given cut by a plane, traces HTV. Find by projection the true shape of the section.
F. A shaped block in third angle is shown, cut by
a plane whose traces are HTV. Draw in first
angle projection, as many views as are required
to find the true shape of the section.

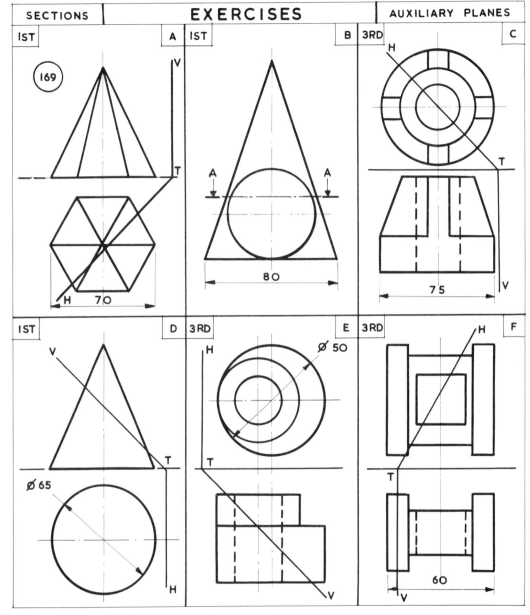

56

TRUE LENGTHS

Plane Traces

Oblique Planes

Triangulation

Developments

170. True Length of Line The pictorial diagram shows a point and four lines projected to the main planes. The true position of the point in (1) is given by simple projection.

In (2), the true length of the line is shown by simple projection as the plane in which the line lies is parallel to the main planes.

In (3), the true length of the line is also shown by simple projection, as the line lies parallel to the main planes.

In (4), the true length is shown only in the plan on the main horizontal plane, as the line lies parallel to the plane; the elevation is foreshortened.

In (5), the true length is shown only in the elevation, as the line lies parallel to the main vertical plane. The view of the line in plan is foreshortened.

First angle projections of the point and lines are shown in the lower diagram. Third angle projections should be done as an exercise.

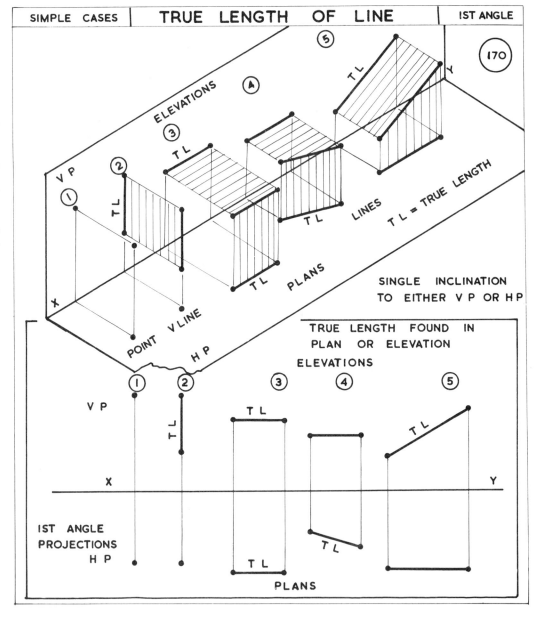

171. True Lengths by Rabatment First angle projections of a triangular lamina are shown in the diagrams. Since the lamina lies on a plane inclined to the main horizontal plane, only the base cb, of the triangle (which is parallel to the main vertical plane) will be true length in the diagrams. The true shape of the triangle could be found by drawing an auxiliary plane parallel to a^2b^2 in the end elevation, and projecting the triangle to this plane, as in 159, 160.

A simpler quicker method is shown in the diagram by 'rabatment'. Draw the plan and elevation as given; project an end elevation. Rabat a^2 to the X Y line by an arc as shown, and project this to the plan. The apex a^4, lies on the intersection of the projector and a perpendicular as shown. Join c and b to a^4 to give the true shape of the lamina. Similarly the point a^2 may be rabated to the front elevation to intersect with a perpendicular as shown, giving again the true shape. Note that the true length of lines, if lying parallel to *neither* of the two main planes, can be found by a *double* rabatment as in 173.

172. True Shape of Lamina In the case of the triangular lamina shown in this diagram, the base, though lying in the horizontal plane, is not parallel to the vertical main plane. To find the true shape, draw the given views, plan and elevation; draw the constructional perpendicular cc^1, and then the perpendicular cd. Project d to d^1, and join to c^1. Project an auxiliary elevation on $X'Y'$, which is parallel to cd. This gives the true length of the perpendicular c^1d^1, which may now be shown as c^3d^1 in the elevation. Join a^1, b^4 and c^3 to give the true shape. Note how b is rabated to a line parallel to the X Y line to give b^4.

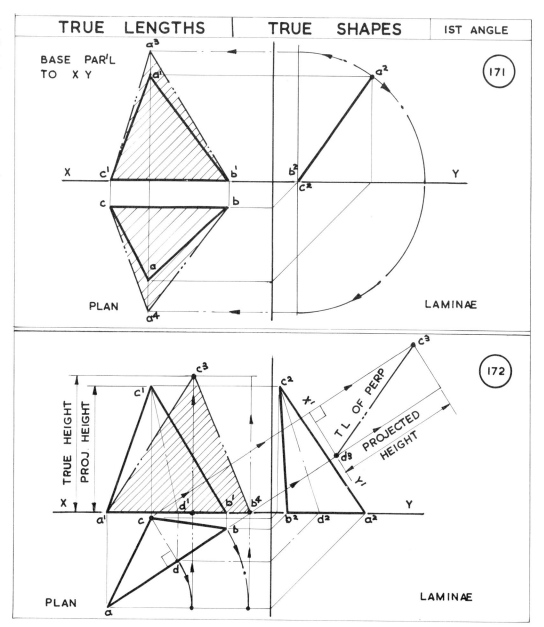

BASE PAR'L TO X Y

171

PLAN

LAMINAE

172

TRUE HEIGHT
PROJ. HEIGHT

T L. OF PERP

PROJECTED HEIGHT

PLAN

LAMINAE

173. True Lengths and the Traces of the Inclined Plane First angle projections and a pictorial explanatory view of a line which is angle to *both* main planes are shown. The plan and elevation of the line are given, and an end elevation can be projected. The line lies in the inclined plane, traces of which are drawn by extending the line from V to give T on the X Y line, and then dropping a perpendicular to meet the extension of the line *ab*. The true length of the line is found by rabating a first to a line parallel to the X Y line, and thence to a line parallel to the X Y line in the elevation, giving a^3. Join a^3 to b^1 to give the true length of the line.

174. True Length of the Line In this case, the extension of the inclined plane lies in the second angle of the projection (see 147). The traces of the plane are shown in the pictorial view for explanation, and the projections shown in the first angle diagram. The true length of the line is found by rabatment as shown, using the method described above.

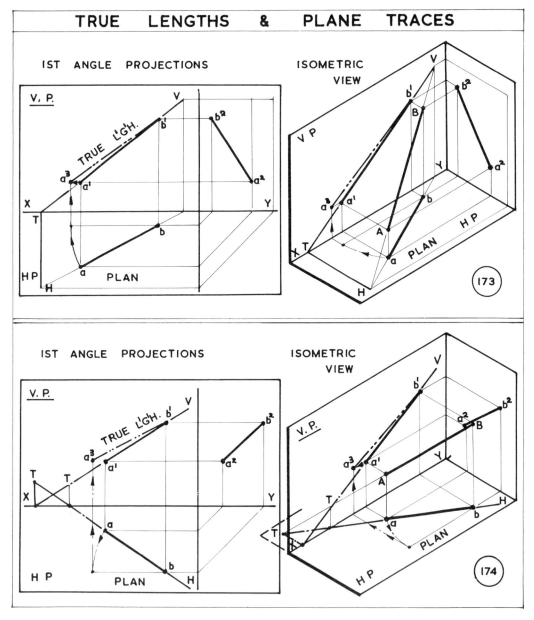

175. True Length of Line and Traces of an inclined plane containing the line. The first angle projections of a line are shown, with a double rabatment to give the true length of the line. In this case the extension of the plane lies in the fourth angle of projection, see small diagram in 147. The complete traces of the plane V T H are found by extending the line until intersections are made with the X Y line and a joining perpendicular. The isometric pictorial view should help to make the details clear.

176. True Length of Line Third angle projections of the line are shown, and double rabatment of the line as before gives the true length of the line.

177. True Length of Line Third angle projections of a line inclined to both main planes of projection are shown with the traces H T V of the auxiliary plane containing it. Double rabatment gives the true length of the line.

Rabatment of projected lines to give the true length form the basis of *Triangulation*, a method of obtaining true shapes in the development of surfaces of geometrical solids, much used by sheet-metal workers in the formation of patterns for the construction of ducts, transition joining pieces, hoods, hoppers etc.; the method is described in detail in 185 to 190.

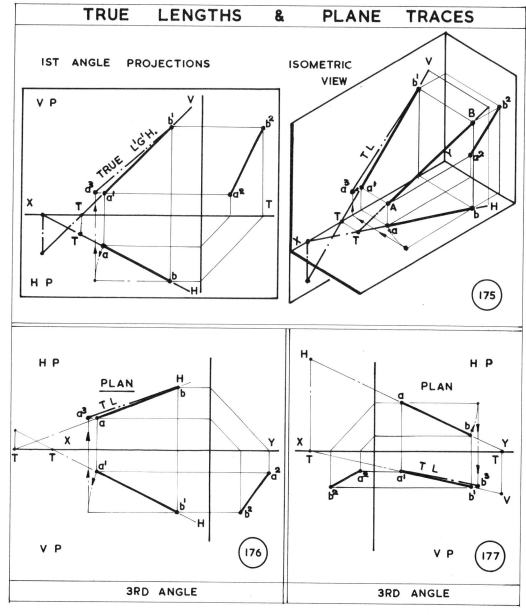

TRUE LENGTHS & PLANE TRACES

1ST ANGLE PROJECTIONS

ISOMETRIC VIEW

175

176

3RD ANGLE

177

3RD ANGLE

178. Oblique Plane Details When an auxiliary plane is inclined to both of the main planes it is said to be an 'oblique plane'. The traces of such a plane will not be at right angles to the X Y line, the angle will be acute or obtuse.

Reference should be made to 181 which gives a pictorial explanatory view of the plane in relation to the main vertical and horizontal planes.

The traces V T H, first angle projection, of an oblique plane are given, with a point P.

179. The True Angles which the plane makes with the main planes, are obtained by rabatment as shown in the diagram. Join V H, and from the point of intersection with the X Y line, draw a line perpendicular to the trace. Rabat the point on the trace to the X Y line, and join to V and H respectively. These are the true angles which the plane makes to the two main planes.

180. Angles Obtained by Auxiliary Planes Draw the traces, the X Y line, and fix the given point in plan. Extend the horizontal trace T H to a convenient distance and draw a new line $X^1 Y^1$, at right angles. Project v^1 to the new line and mark off the height as H from the front elevation—*heights unchanged*—for all elevations. Draw in the line showing the inclined plane—which is an edge or end-on view of the oblique plane. Project the point P from the plan to the inclined plane line, P^1. The height of the point is shown by H^1 and this height can now be brought back to the main elevation to cut off a projection line from the point in plan, thus establishing the position of P^2.

Laminae can be projected using this method by taking each point in turn and projecting either to an auxiliary elevation or plan and joining up. See 182.

If the trace V T is extended, and a new $X^2 Y^2$ line drawn, an auxiliary plan may be drawn, widths remaining the same as in the original plan, as shown in the diagram.

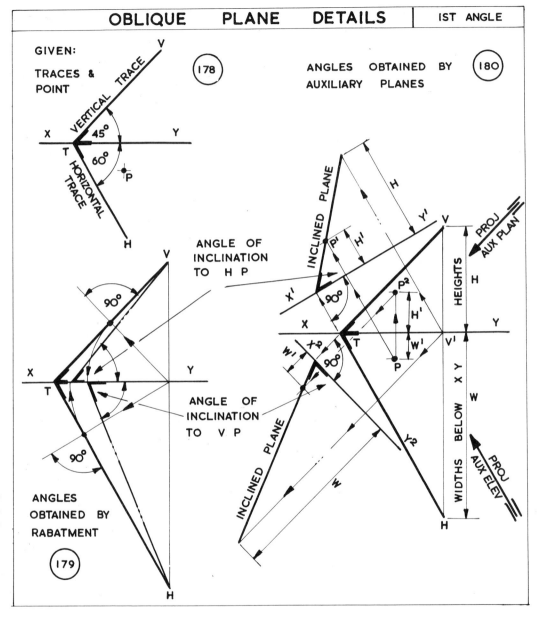

62

181. Oblique Plane Projections The traces and plan of a triangular lamina are given as shown. Draw the elevation and find the true shape of the lamina. First angle projection.

182. Solution Draw the traces, the X Y line and the plan as given. Extend the trace T H to a convenient length, draw the new X^1Y^1 line at right angles to the trace. Project V to give height H in the auxiliary elevation, enabling the inclined plane to be drawn. Project the three points of the lamina from the plan to the inclined plane, thus obtaining L, L^1 and L^2. To obtain the true shape of the lamina, the three lengths must be used in a projection from the plan, as shown in the diagram.

The elevation of the lamina uses heights obtained from the inclined plane and are H^1, H^2, H^3. The three points of the lamina are projected from the plan to the elevation, and the projectors cut off to these heights respectively. The details are shown in the diagram.

The projections should be drawn two or three times the printed size as a first exercise before attempting the exercises on page 65.

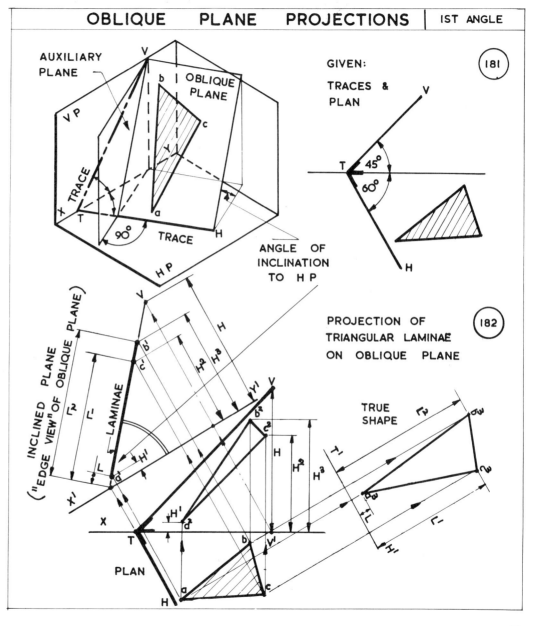

OBLIQUE PLANE PROJECTIONS | 1ST ANGLE

AUXILIARY PLANE

OBLIQUE PLANE

GIVEN:
TRACES & PLAN

ANGLE OF INCLINATION TO H P

181

PROJECTION OF TRIANGULAR LAMINAE ON OBLIQUE PLANE

182

("EDGE VIEW" OF OBLIQUE PLANE)
INCLINED PLANE

LAMINAE

TRUE SHAPE

PLAN

183. True Shape of a Triangle Given the projections of a triangle, find the true shape and angle to the horizontal plane.

Solution Draw the plan and elevation as given. Draw the horizontal construction line cd, project the plan to give c^1d^1. Extend C^1d^1 and draw a new X^1Y^1 line at right angles. Project from a^1 to give a^2, making the height H^2, the same height as a in the elevation. Project b^1 and c^1 to this inclined plane, which gives an edge view of the triangle. Points a^2, b^2, c^2 are the points of the triangle on the inclined plane.

Draw now a new X^2Y^2 line, parallel to the line of the inclined plane; project a new plan from this X^2Y^2 line, making W, W^2, W^3 widths from the line. This will give points from which the true shape of the triangle can be drawn. Note that c^3 and d^3 are in the same line.

The true angle of the plane of the triangle to the horizontal plane is shown at the angle of the X^1Y^1 line and the inclined plane in the auxiliary elevation.

This method may be used when the traces of the plane are not given in the problem.

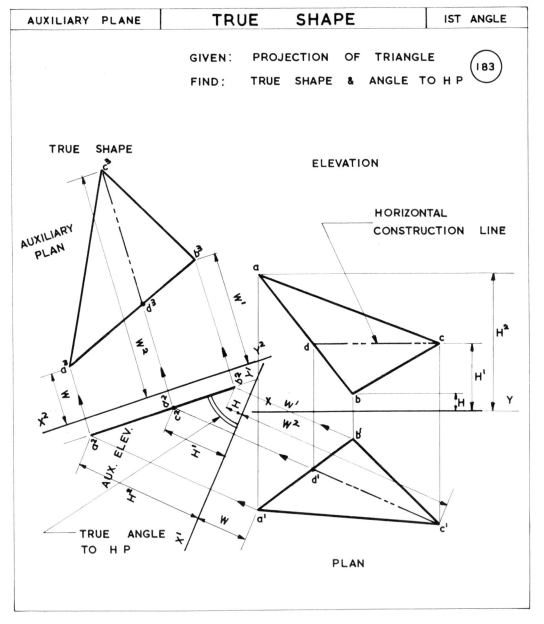

GIVEN: PROJECTION OF TRIANGLE

FIND: TRUE SHAPE & ANGLE TO HP

183

TRUE SHAPE

ELEVATION

HORIZONTAL CONSTRUCTION LINE

AUXILIARY PLAN

AUX. ELEV.

TRUE ANGLE TO HP

PLAN

184. A. The projections of a line are given in first angle projection; draw the given line, project an end elevation, and find the true length.

B. The projections of a line are given in third angle; draw the plan and elevation as given, project an end elevation and find the true length by rabatment.

C. The plan and elevation of a lamina are given. By the method shown in 183, find the true shape and the true inclination to the horizontal plane. First angle.

D. Third angle details of a plane and a point P are shown. Using the method in 180, draw the position of P on both the main planes.

E. First angle projections of a lamina and the traces of the oblique plane containing it are given. Draw the plan and elevation; find the true shape. (182)

F. A cube is cut by an oblique plane the traces of which are given. First angle. (Draw the views, extend VT and draw a new auxiliary plan.)

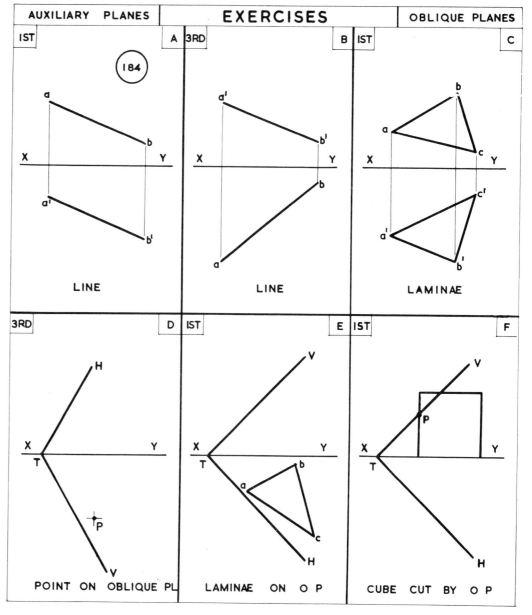

| AUXILIARY PLANES | EXERCISES | OBLIQUE PLANES |

184

LINE — LINE — LAMINÆ

POINT ON OBLIQUE PL — LAMINÆ ON O P — CUBE CUT BY O P

185. Oblique Pyramid: Development by Triangulation

The plan and elevation of an oblique octagonal pyramid are given. Draw the development after finding the true length of the meeting facets. (The term 'oblique' in this case has no connection with the foregoing pages on the oblique plane.)

The oblique solids—pyramid, cone, prism, cylinder—have a regular shape for the base, and the axis of the solid is not at right angles to its base. (As different from say, a right cone, which has its axis at right angles to its base.)

It should be clear from the first angle projections given in the diagram, that only two generators of the pyramid, A4 and A0, are shown in true length, as they are seen in true elevation. Generators A1, A2, A3, require their true length to be found by rabatment. A half plan is drawn as a construction touching the elevation, and an arc is described to cut the extension of the XY line in 1′ as shown. A1′ is the true length of A1. Find true lengths A2′, A3′, by the same method. (The sides of the base octagon in the plan are true length and require no rabatment.)

The development of the surface of the pyramid may now be drawn. Draw A4′ as the starting line. Draw A3′ as an arc from A; cut by an arc from 4′, radius 3–4 (from the plane). Build up the development in this way, each side being a triangle of true lengths.

A section line Z Z, is shown cutting the pyramid; the true lengths of the generators at the cutting plane are found by projection across to the true lengths; these can be now stepped off along the respective true length from A in the development. The full development of the pyramid would include the base octagon. Draw side length 40 mm.

This development, as with others in the following pages, should be made on thick drawing paper or thin card, cut out and pasted together to form the solid.

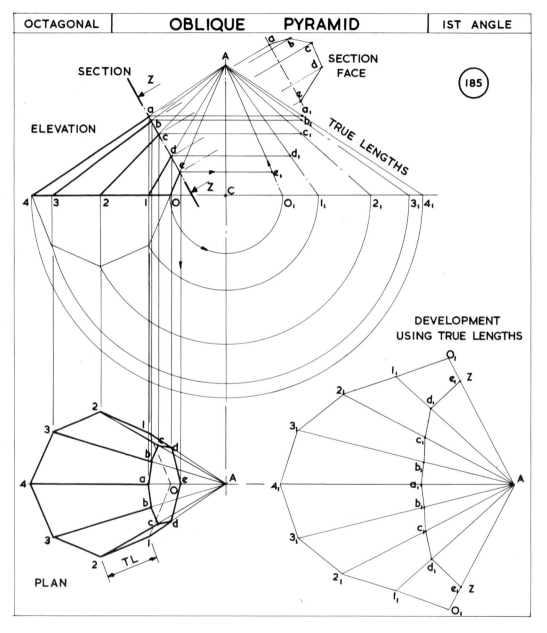

185

186. Oblique Cone: Development by Triangulation

The first angle projections of an oblique cone are given. Find the true lengths of the generators, and draw the development of the surface of the cone.

Draw the given plan and elevation. Note that the base of the cone is a circle, and that the axis is not at right angles to the base. Divide the base circle into twelve parts using a setsquare, project these to the elevation, and draw the generators in the elevation. Draw the constructional semicircle under the elevation, and project the points of intersection to find true lengths at A0', A1', A2', A3', A5', of the generators. A0 and A6 are the true length already. Chordal distances from the plan on the base circle, 0–1, 1–2, etc. are usually allowed as true lengths for use in the development.

Start the development by drawing A6'; with centre A, and radius A5' describe an arc, to be cut by an arc from 6', radius 6'–5'. This gives the triangle of the first twelfth of the surface of the cone. Proceed, using true lengths of generators and base circle chordal lengths, to draw the rest of the development as shown in the diagram.

Two section lines are shown in the elevation at W and Z. Project the point of intersection of the cuts with the generators to the true lengths as shown, and step off these lengths from A in the development. Note that, since this is a cone development, the points are joined by a fair curve.

As in 185, the development should be cut out and joined up to form the solid to prove the method. The base circle completes the development. The diagram can be drawn to any convenient size, a base circle 10 cm in diameter is suggested.

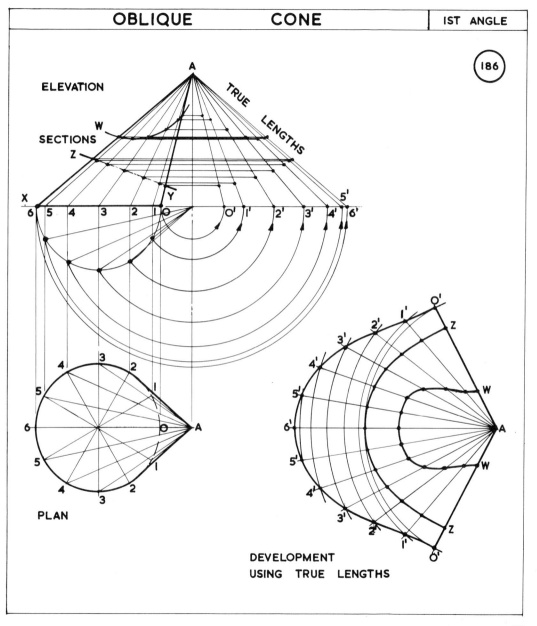

186

ELEVATION

TRUE LENGTHS

SECTIONS

W

Z

X   Y

6 5 4 3 2 1 O   O' 1' 2' 3' 4' 6'   5'

PLAN

DEVELOPMENT
USING TRUE LENGTHS

187. Development by Triangulation of a Hood or Hopper First angle projections are shown of a hood to be made in sheet metal, or if inverted, a hopper for directing a flow in a duct.

The base rectangle lies on the main horizontal plane, the lengths of the sides are therefore true length as shown. The upper rectangle is also true. The quadrilaterals forming the sides of the hood are not parallel to the main planes and do not show their true shapes. Lengths must be found by rabatment. The true width of side A is rabated to the plan, and combined with the true lengths of the base and top edges; the true shape is shown. The sides B and C are shown rabated in the same way.

The true shape of the sides may also be found by triangulation. A diagonal line is drawn in each side, and the true length of each line found by rabatment from a point as in 185 and 186.

188. Development of the Hood (shown in the diagrams). Draw side A first; if the first method is used, the diagonal enables the quadrilateral to be drawn as two triangles by use of arcs. Finish the development by adding sides B, C and B.

Further similar problems follow on pages 69–72.

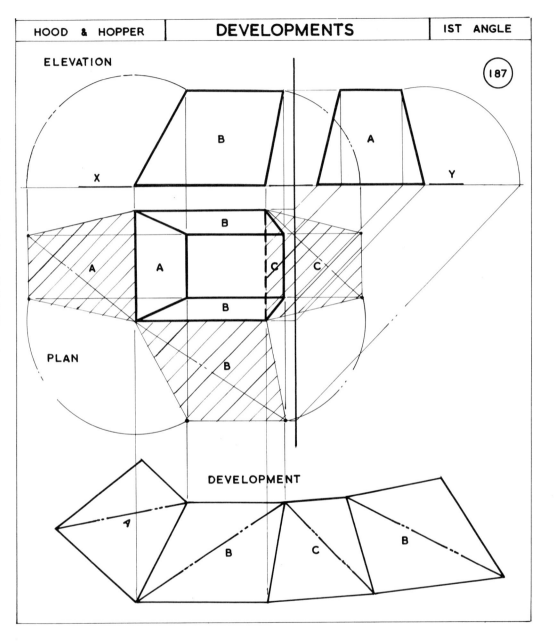

ELEVATION

187

X   Y

B   A

PLAN

A   A   B   C   C   B   B

DEVELOPMENT

A   B   C   B

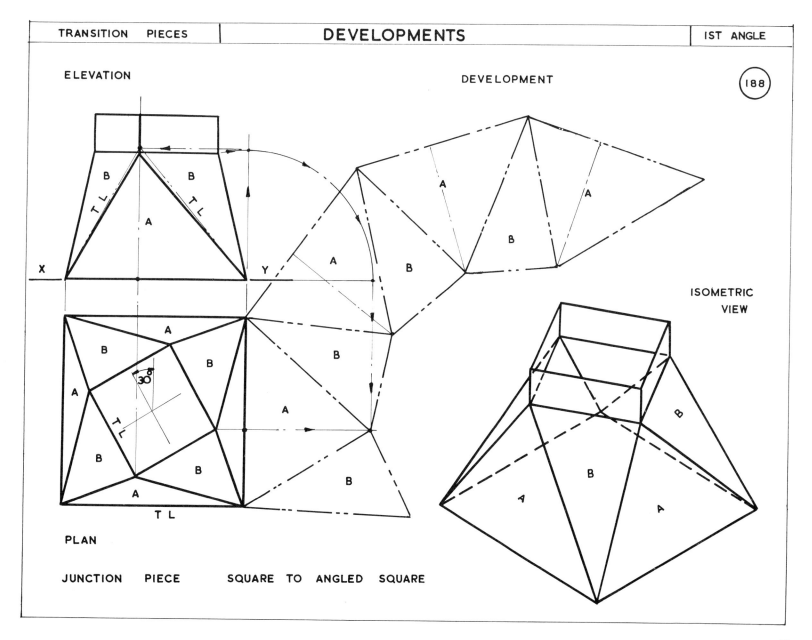

ELEVATION

DEVELOPMENT

(188)

ISOMETRIC VIEW

PLAN

JUNCTION PIECE   SQUARE TO ANGLED SQUARE

69

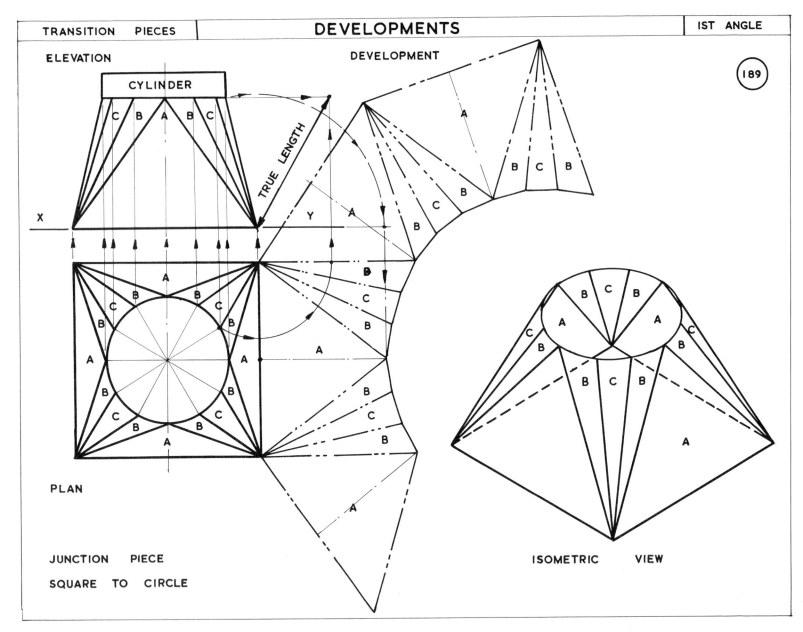

ELEVATION

CYLINDER

C B A B C

DEVELOPMENT

189

TRUE LENGTH

X   Y

A

B

C

B

A

PLAN

JUNCTION PIECE

SQUARE TO CIRCLE

ISOMETRIC VIEW

189. Development of Transition Piece by Triangulation and Rabatment First angle projections of a transition or junction moving from a square to a circle. Sides of the lower square are true lengths. The top circle is divided radially into twelve parts by setsquare. These division points are joined to the ends of the square, resulting in triangles A, B, C. The circle divisions may be chordal, or their length calculated by $3\frac{1}{7} \times$ diameter.

The true height of side A may be rabated from the elevation to the plan to meet the perpendicular from the side of the square base, giving in turn the shape of the triangular side A. Rabat the side of B as shown in the diagram. The triangle B has one side in common with A, the second side common with C, and the third small side the chordal part of the circle.

Draw side A first, and by arcs using true lengths, construct the triangles of B and C in the order shown.

Construct the model from the development, pasting together by adding flaps at the outer ends.

190. Development of Junction Piece by Triangulation First angle projections of the junction piece show a square base moving to an offset circle. The top circle is divided into the usual twelve parts, and the points joined to the ends of the base square. Draw the plan and elevation, as shown. Number the points on the circle.

Label the corners of the square A, B, C, D, and use these as centres for the rabatment of the point on the circle as shown. After drawing the arcs, project to the elevation, and obtain the true lengths of all the sides of the triangles. The actual development can now be drawn as an exercise.

N.B. In triangulation, it should now be seen that the true length is really the hypotenuse of its own triangle, and rabatment is the easy method of drawing that special triangle.

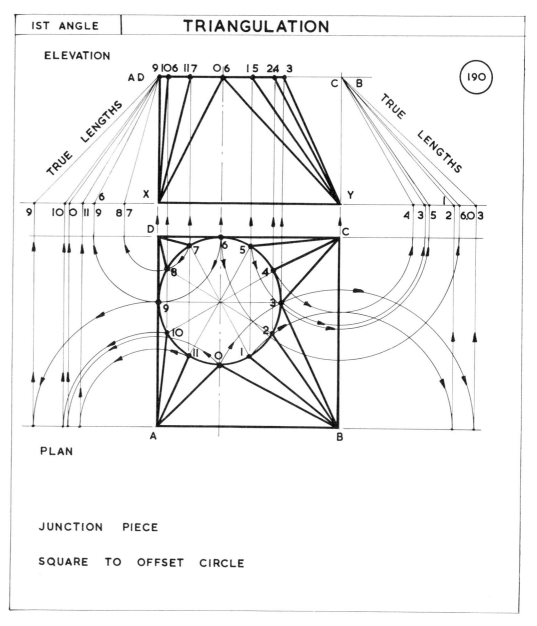

ELEVATION

TRUE LENGTHS

TRUE LENGTHS

PLAN

JUNCTION PIECE

SQUARE TO OFFSET CIRCLE

191. Exercises for Triangulation

A. A transition piece which moves from an octagon to a square is shown. Obtain the true lengths of the triangles; draw the development.

B. The elevation of a hood which has a base circle and an angled square at the top. Draw the elevation given, project a plan. Divide the base circle into twelve parts, join the points to the corners of the square. Obtain the true lengths of the triangles composing the development and construct the development.

C. A hood is shown which has a base circle moving to a top square. Draw the given elevation, and project a plan. Divide the base circle into twelve parts, join the points to the corners of the square. Obtain the true lengths of the sides of the triangles in the development, and draw the development.

D. The elevation of a hood is shown, having a base circle moving to an angled square. The diagram may be simplified by drawing the base circle lying in the horizontal plane. Proceed as in B above.

E. Two views of a hopper are shown. Draw the development.

F. Two views of a hood are shown. Draw the views, obtain the true lengths required, and draw the development, including the flat back portion.

Areas and Volumes of Simple Solids

192. Cube.

193. Rectangular prism.

194. Regular prism.

195. Cylinder.

196. Right Cone.

197. Sphere.

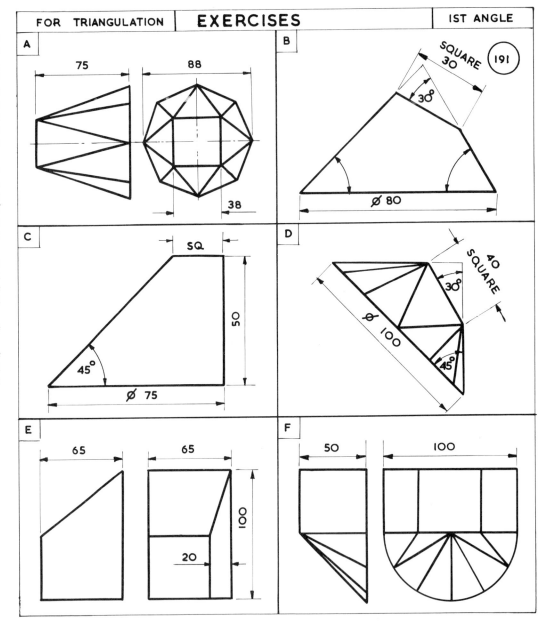

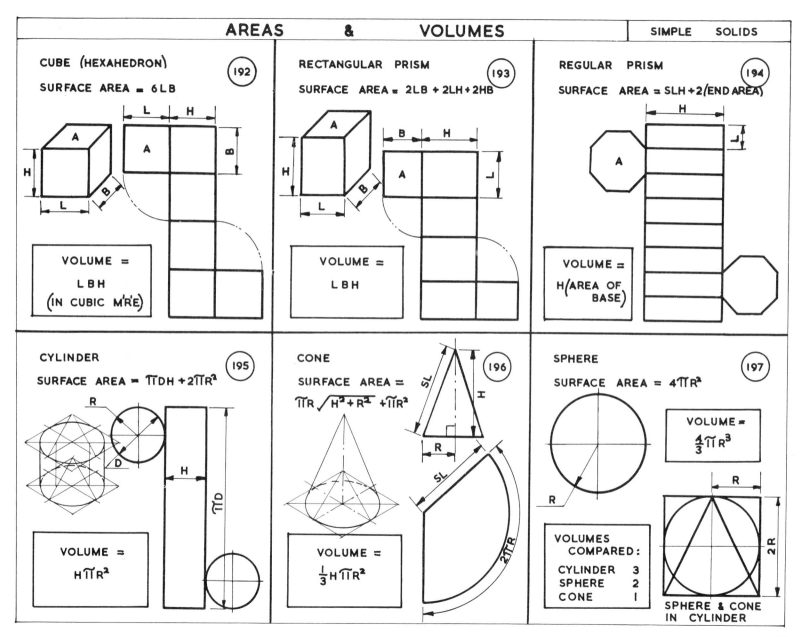

AREAS & VOLUMES

CUBE (HEXAHEDRON) (192)

SURFACE AREA = 6LB

VOLUME =
L B H
(IN CUBIC M'R'E)

RECTANGULAR PRISM (193)

SURFACE AREA = 2LB + 2LH + 2HB

VOLUME =
L B H

REGULAR PRISM (194)

SURFACE AREA = SLH + 2(END AREA)

VOLUME =
H(AREA OF BASE)

CYLINDER (195)

SURFACE AREA = $\pi DH + 2\pi R^2$

VOLUME =
$H \pi R^2$

CONE (196)

SURFACE AREA =
$\pi R \sqrt{H^2 + R^2} + \pi R^2$

VOLUME =
$\frac{1}{3} H \pi R^2$

SPHERE (197)

SURFACE AREA = $4\pi R^2$

VOLUME =
$\frac{4}{3} \pi R^3$

VOLUMES COMPARED:

CYLINDER 3
SPHERE   2
CONE   1

SPHERE & CONE
IN CYLINDER

198. Developments by Linear Method First angle plan and elevation of shaped hood are given. Though the profile is shaped, the sections parallel to the horizontal plane are rectangular.

The development of the faces can be obtained by dividing the profile into convenient small divisions in the elevation, and projecting the points to the plan and thence into the extended face which is the true shape. Face A is given as an example. The front face may be developed in a similar manner.

199. Development by Linear Method First angle views of the object are given. An auxiliary view which gives the true projected shape of one is also required as shown. The surface of the semi-cylindrical shape is given by the use of generators.

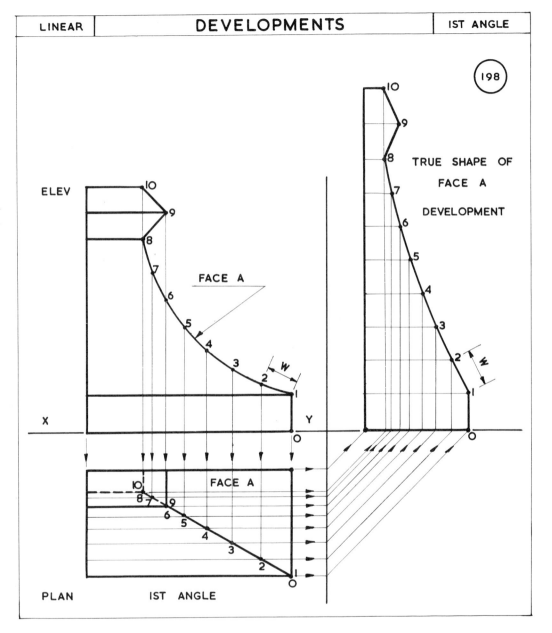

TRUE SHAPE OF FACE A

DEVELOPMENT

ELEV

FACE A

X   Y

PLAN   1ST ANGLE

FACE A

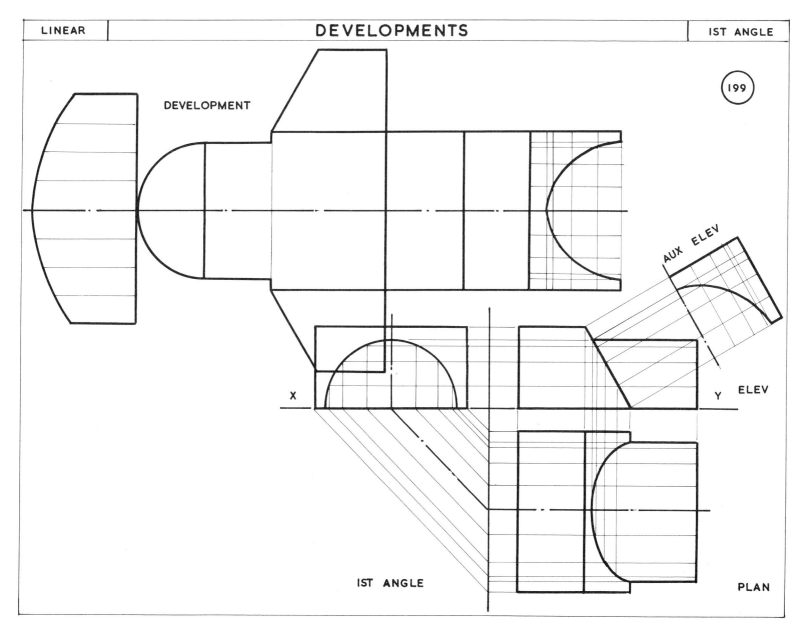

DEVELOPMENT

199

AUX ELEV

Y ELEV

X

1ST ANGLE

PLAN

75

200. Development of Tetrahedron The true length of the side of the triangle is found by triangulation, see 190. The development is four equilateral triangles.

201. Development of Octahedron The true length of the side of the eight triangles is found by rabatment as shown. The development is also shown.

202. Development of Dodecahedron The solid has twelve sides, each is a regular pentagon. The plan shows the true shape of the pentagon. The sides require to be drawn in the sequence shown, pasting flaps should be added if the model is to be constructed.

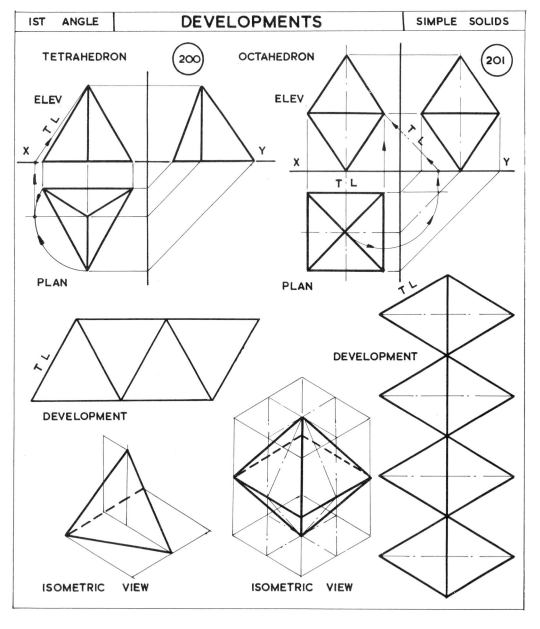

TETRAHEDRON   200   OCTAHEDRON   201

ELEV

PLAN

DEVELOPMENT

ISOMETRIC VIEW

ELEV

TL

PLAN

DEVELOPMENT

ISOMETRIC VIEW

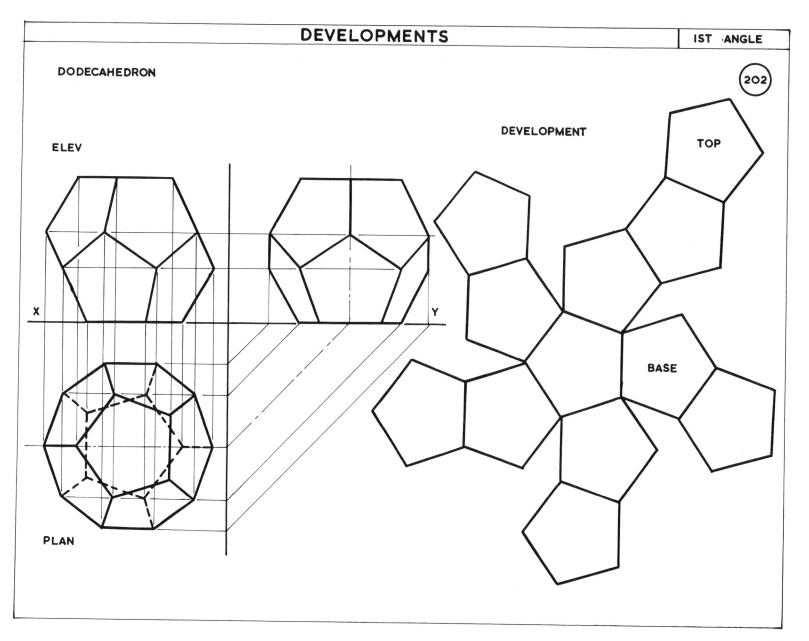

DODECAHEDRON

202

ELEV

DEVELOPMENT

TOP

X

Y

BASE

PLAN

203. Exercises for Linear Development

A. First angle views. Draw proportionately from the one dimension given. Draw the development.
B. First angle. Draw the views; draw the development.
C. Third angle views are given. Draw the development.
D. First angle views are shown. Draw the development.
E. First angle views are given. Draw the development.
F. Third angle views. Draw the development.
G. First angle views. Draw the development.
H. Third angle views. Draw the development.
I. Third angle views. Draw the development.

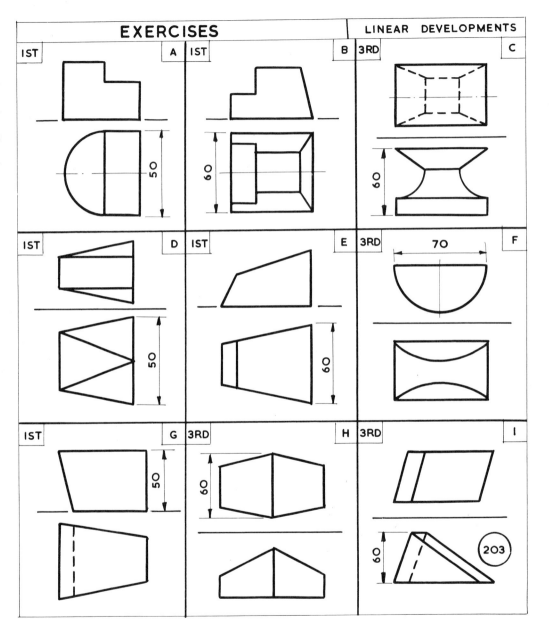

INTERPENETRATION

Cylinders

Prisms

Pyramids

Cones

Spheres

Palmate

Solids of Revolution

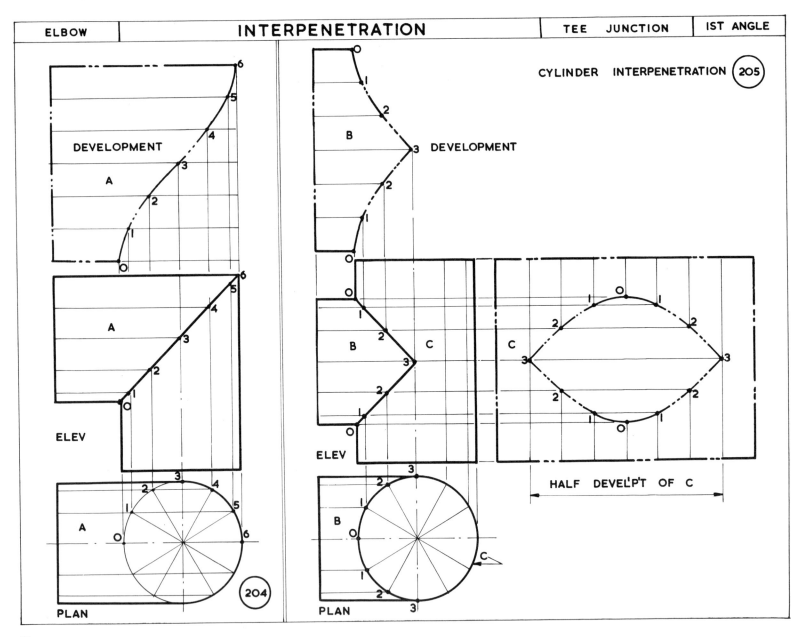

CYLINDER INTERPENETRATION (205)

DEVELOPMENT

A

DEVELOPMENT

B

DEVELOPMENT

A

ELEV

B

C

C

C

HALF DEVEL'P'T OF C

A

PLAN

(204)

B

PLAN

ELEV

204. Elbow Two cylinders of equal diameter meeting at right angles. First angle projections are given. The circle of the cylinder is divided into twelve parts by setsquare, and the generators projected into the elevation. Since the two cylinders are of equal diameter, the same projectors will do for both cylinders. The line of intersection will be a straight line.

The development of A piece is best projected in line with its cylinder as shown. The divisions of the opened out cylinder may be chordal, from the cylinder circle; or may be calculated $3\frac{1}{7} \times D$. The labelled points of intersection 0, 1, 2, 3, 4, 5, 6, are projected to the cylinder development, to cut the respective generators. A fair curve through the points completes the development which is symmetrical and only half is shown.

205. Tee Junction of two equal diameter cylinders. First angle plan and elevation are given. Proceed as above, dividing the circle into 12 parts for projecting generators whose intersections give the line of the interpenetration. Part B is developed in line as before. Part C is developed also in line with its cylinder; the points on the intersection line being projected to the respective division. Note the shape of the hole in cylinder C.

206. Equal Cylinders at Right Angles First angle views of the interpenetration are given, note the crossed straight line of the intersection. Draw the construction circle and the generators. Develop the one piece only, as all the four portions are equal. Only a half portion is shown.

The above diagram should be drawn to any convenient size: a diameter of 50 to 80 mm would be suitable.

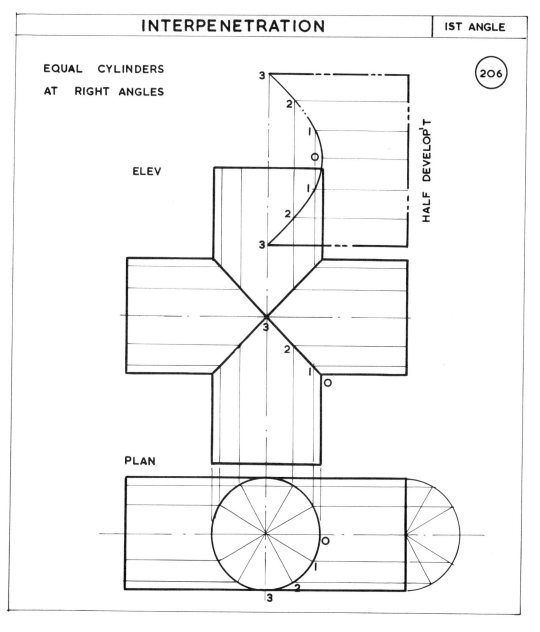

EQUAL CYLINDERS
AT RIGHT ANGLES

206

HALF DEVELOP'T

ELEV

PLAN

81

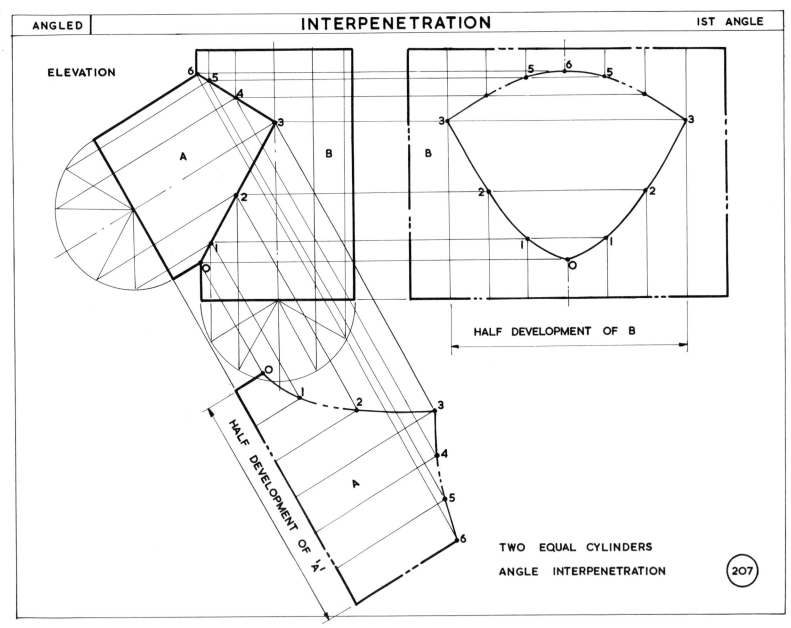

ELEVATION

A

B

B

HALF DEVELOPMENT OF B

HALF DEVELOPMENT OF 'A'

A

TWO EQUAL CYLINDERS

ANGLE INTERPENETRATION

207

207. Two Equal Cylinders at an Angle First angle views are given to two equal diameter cylinders which interpenetrate at an angle of 60°. When the axis lines lie in the same plane, the term 'co-axial' is applied.

Draw the given views to a convenient size. Draw the constructional semicircles, project the generators to obtain the line of intersection. The development of A piece should be in line with its cylinder as shown. The development of B piece should be in line with its cylinder. Note the shape of the aperture in B.

208. Three Cylinders Interpenetrating at 120° The first angle views of the interpenetration are given. Draw the constructional circles and generators. This gives the straight line intersection. Project the development in line with one of the cylinders. A symmetrical half-portion only is shown.

The above developments can be made using diameters of 50 mm to 80 mm, and can be constructed in thick paper and pasted together after adding pasting flaps.

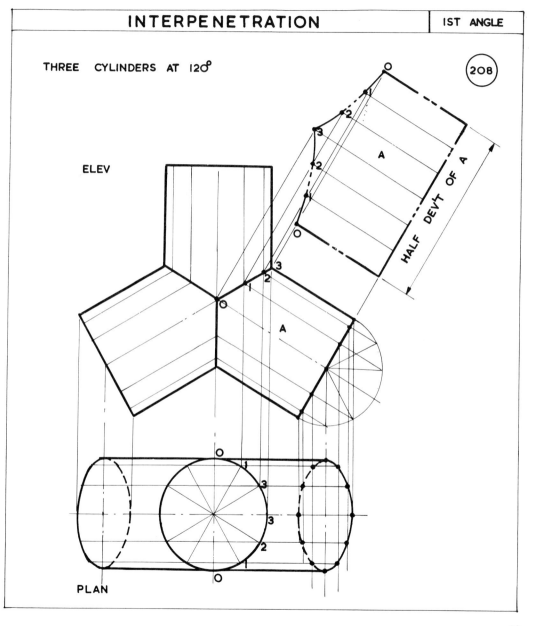

THREE CYLINDERS AT 120°

208

ELEV

HALF DEV'T OF A

A

PLAN

209. Two Cylinders of Unequal Diameters at right angles first angle views of the interpenetration are given. Draw the given views; draw the constructional semicircles and the generators of the smaller diameter cylinder. Project the points of intersection with the larger cylinder 0, 1, 2, 3, to the elevation, meeting the respective generators there. Draw a fair curve through the points of intersection in the elevation. The development of B can now be projected in line with B cylinder.

The development of the larger cylinder should be projected in line with its cylinder. Note that chordal widths can be taken from the plan at 3, 2, 1, 0, for use on the opened out cylinder to intersect with projectors from the elevation. The penetration is co-axial.

210. Angled Co-axial Interpenetration of two unequal diameter cylinders. Plan and elevation in first angle projection are given. Draw the views, constructional semicircles, and generators of the smaller cylinders. Label the points of intersection in the plan. Project these to the elevation to give the line of intersection of the two cylinders. Project the development of B cylinder in line with its cylinder, as shown.

Project the development of the larger diameter cylinder in line; chordal widths must be taken from the plan for use on the development. Note that the two apertures are identical.

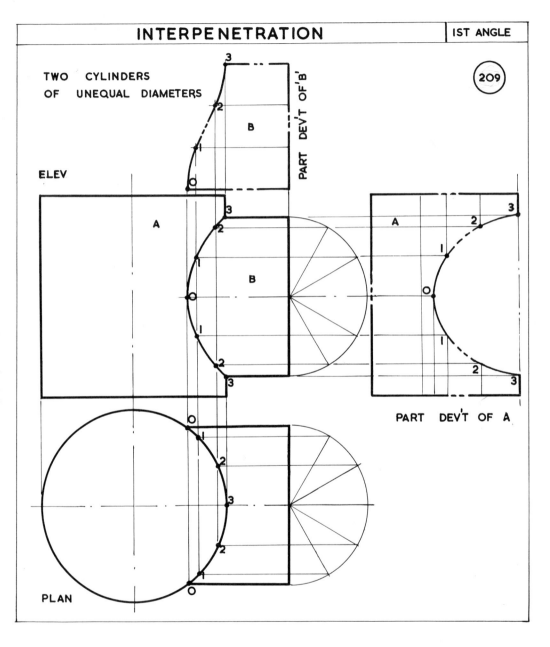

INTERPENETRATION   IST ANGLE

TWO CYLINDERS OF UNEQUAL DIAMETERS

209

PART DEV'T OF 'B'

ELEV

A

B

PART DEV'T OF A

PLAN

INTERPENETRATION

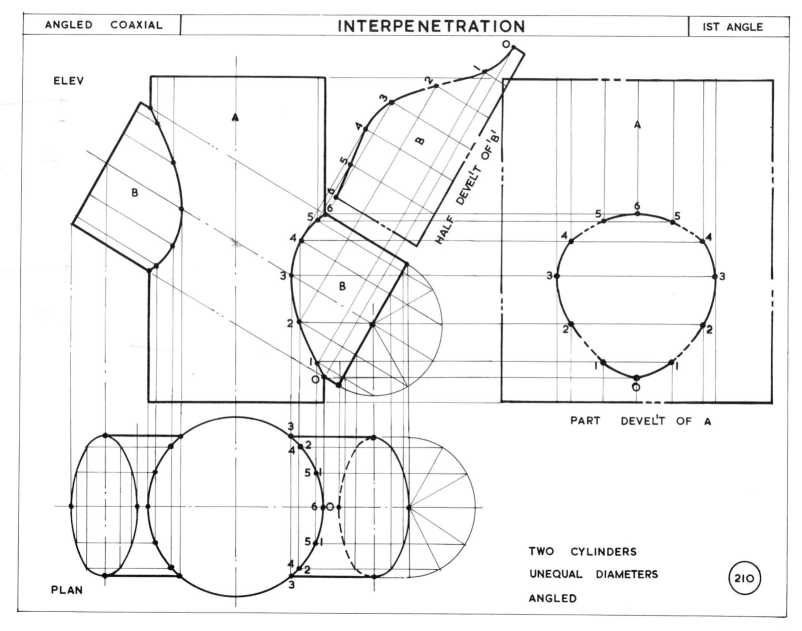

ELEV

A

B

B

B

HALF DEVEL'T OF 'B'

PART DEVEL'T OF A

A

PLAN

TWO CYLINDERS

UNEQUAL DIAMETERS

ANGLED

210

85

211. Offset Interpenetration of Two Unequal Cylinders First angle views are shown of the interpenetration of two cylinders of unequal diameters, whose axes are not in the same plane, and so are said to be 'offset'.

Draw the plan and elevation; draw the constructional semicircles and generators of the smaller cylinder. Label the points of intersection in the plan, and project to the elevation. Draw the curve of intersection. Project part B in line with its cylinder. Project the development of A in line with its cylinder. Chordal widths must be taken from the plan to be used on the development. Note the shape of the aperture.

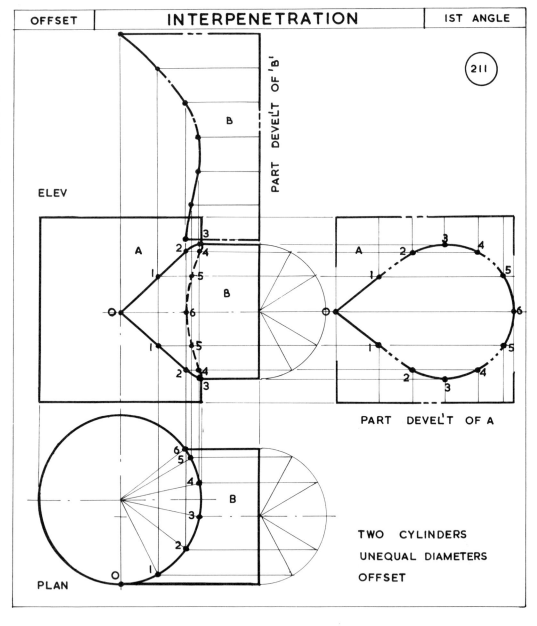

PART DEVEL'T OF 'B'

211

ELEV

A

B

B

PART DEVEL'T OF A

A

B

PLAN

TWO CYLINDERS
UNEQUAL DIAMETERS
OFFSET

212. Prism and Cylinder Interpenetration First angle views are given of a cylinder being pierced by a square prism at right angles, offset, the prism being tilted slightly.

Draw the plan, elevation and end elevation. Project the corners of the square from the end elevation to the plan and thence to the front elevation. By suitable cylinder generators from the plan, the various intersection points can be obtained and joined to give the lines of intersection as shown in the drawing.

The cylinder development is shown in line with the elevation of the cylinder. Chordal widths being taken from the plan.

Owing to limitation of paper space, the two faces of the prism have been superimposed, but these should be drawn in line from the elevation.

Note that the generators of the cylinder each have two intersection points, one for the upper face, and one for the lower face of the prism. Construct the model in paper from the developments.

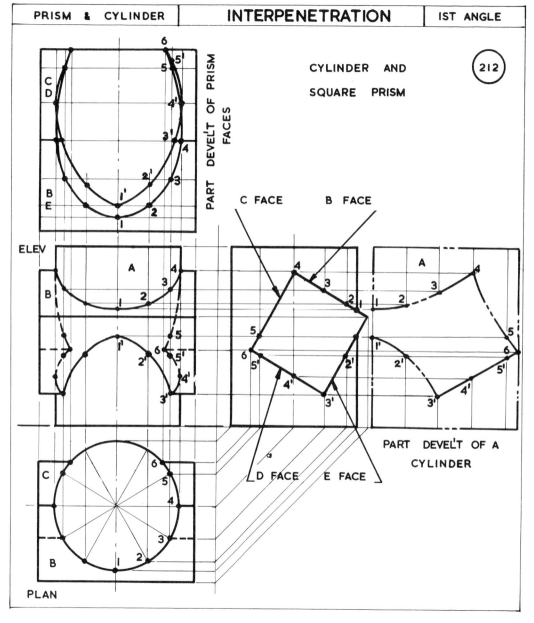

CYLINDER AND
SQUARE PRISM

212

PART DEVEL'T OF PRISM FACES

ELEV

C FACE   B FACE

D FACE   E FACE

PART DEVEL'T OF A CYLINDER

PLAN

87

213. Two Square Prisms Offset Third angle views of the interpenetration are given. Points on the end elevation should be projected to the plan and elevation; note that the projections of all the points form complete circuits in the views, and each point shown in the diagrams should be traced through in sequence.

Note that when two prisms having plane faces meet, the intersection lines will be straight lines.

Draw the views two or three times the printed size. The model may be constructed from the developments which are left as an exercise.

214. Square Pyramid Piercing a Triangular Prism First angle views are given of the interpenetration. Simple projection in this case will give points to be joined to give lines (straight) of intersection. The detail drawing shows how the pyramid development is made.

Note that the true length of the line of the meeting faces of the pyramid is obtained by rabatment. See 185.

The development of the prism is best projected in line with the prism as shown.

The development of the pyramid can be best drawn in line from the pyramid, but note that the arc of the enclosing sector has the true length as radius.

The model can be constructed from the developments. Draw at least twice the printed size.

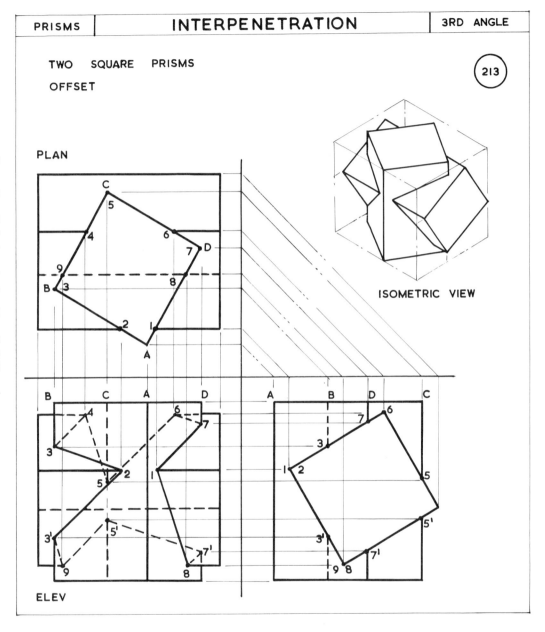

TWO SQUARE PRISMS OFFSET

PLAN

ELEV

ISOMETRIC VIEW

213

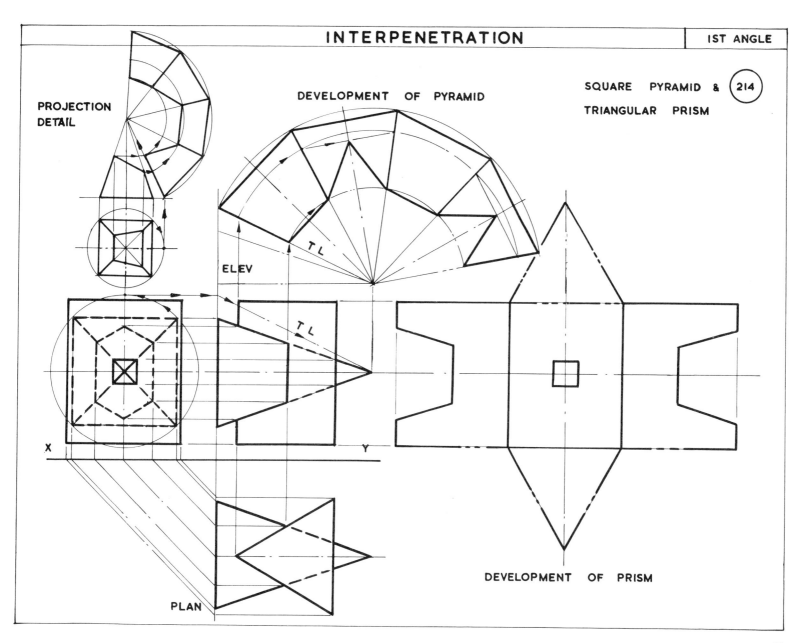

INTERPENETRATION

SQUARE PYRAMID & 214
TRIANGULAR PRISM

PROJECTION
DETAIL

DEVELOPMENT OF PYRAMID

ELEV

T L

T L

X

Y

PLAN

DEVELOPMENT OF PRISM

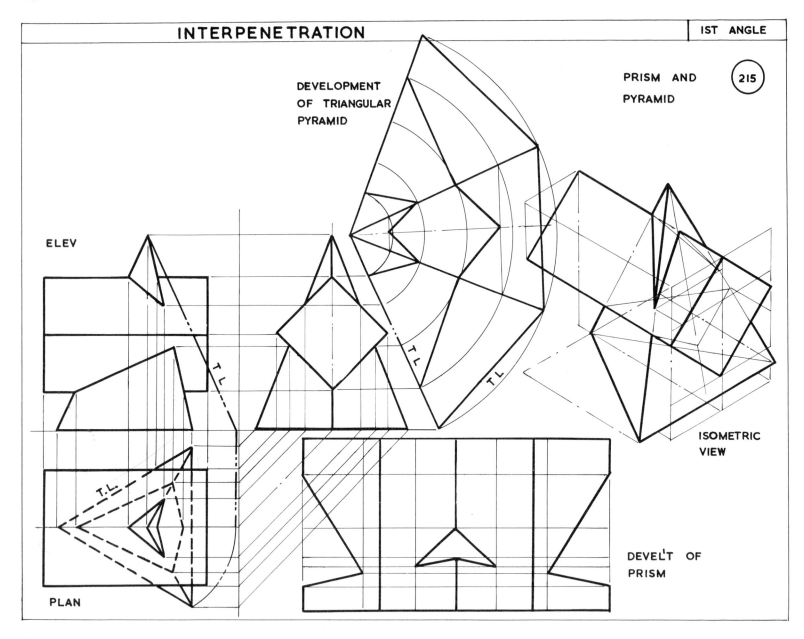

DEVELOPMENT
OF TRIANGULAR
PYRAMID

PRISM AND
PYRAMID

215

ELEV

T L

T L

T L

ISOMETRIC
VIEW

T.L.

PLAN

DEVEL'T OF
PRISM

215. Square Prism pierced by Triangular Pyramid axes at right angles. First angle views are given together with the development of both prism and pyramid.

Draw the three views shown, project the points of intersection and draw in the lines of intersection. The development of the pyramid may now be drawn; note that it is necessary to rabat the corner of the base to obtain the true length of the slope line of the pyramid which is then used as the radius of the enclosing sector of the development. The true lengths of the base are shown in plan, and can be stepped off as chords in the arc, giving the points of the three sides in the development.

The development of the prism would be best projected in line with the prism from the elevation, though in the diagram it has been shown below because of printing space.

216. Rectangular Pyramid and Cylinder A hood or transition piece using a cylinder and a pyramid are shown in first angle.

Draw the given views, draw the generators in the cylinder. Obtain by projection, the lines of intersection of the two solids. Find the true lengths of the angle lines of the pyramid by rabatment as shown. The development of side A is shown in the diagram. The development of the other two sides of the pyramid and the development of the surface of the cylinder is left as an exercise. Project the development of the cylinder in line with the elevation.

The two interpenetrations can be constructed as models from the development. Use thick paper, pasted together, leaving flaps for this purpose.

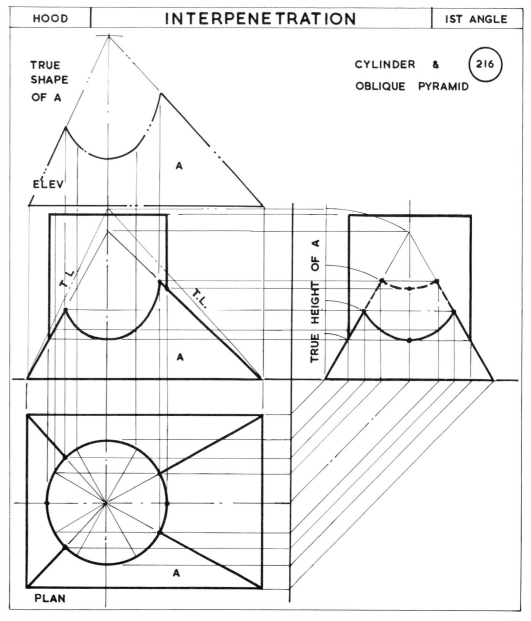

CYLINDER & 216
OBLIQUE PYRAMID

TRUE SHAPE OF A

ELEV

T.L

T.L.

A

A

TRUE HEIGHT OF A

PLAN

217. Interpenetration of Hexagonal Prism and a Hexagonal Pyramid Three first angle views of the interpenetration are given showing the lines of intersection. Draw the views in third angle projection, and then make the developments of the surfaces of the two solids. Project each in line as in previous examples.

218. The Interpenetration of a Cylinder and a Half-Octagonal Pyramid is shown in third angle projection. Draw the example in first angle projection. Project the points and lines of intersection. Draw the developments of the cylinder and the part pyramid, each in line with its solid.

Make the model from the developments.

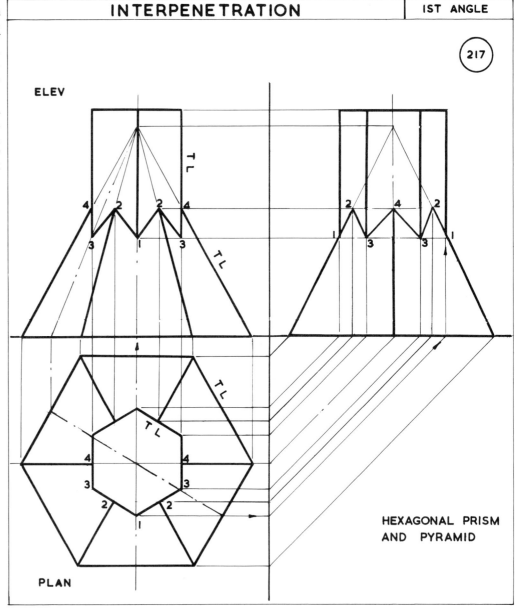

ELEV

TL

TL

TL

PLAN

TL

HEXAGONAL PRISM AND PYRAMID

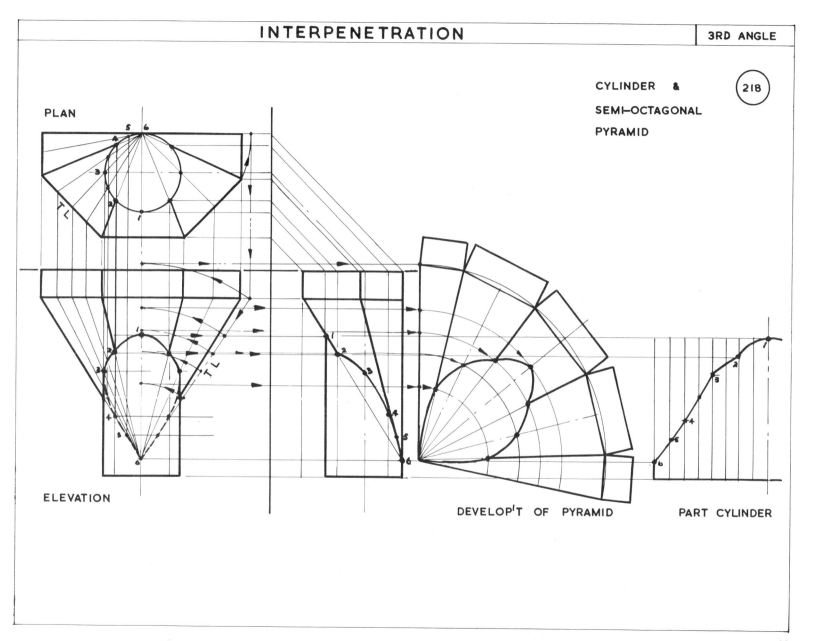

INTERPENETRATION

CYLINDER &
SEMI—OCTAGONAL
PYRAMID

218

PLAN

ELEVATION

DEVELOP'T OF PYRAMID

PART CYLINDER

93

219. Cone and Cylinder Interpenetration (First Case) The three usual cases of cone and cylinder interpenetrations are shown on the next three pages.

In this first diagram, two generators of the cone are tangential to the circle of the cylinder. This can be seen in the end elevation. The lines of intersection are crossed straight lines passing through this tangential point in the elevation. In the plan, the lines of intersection are two intersecting ellipses.

Draw the three views given; draw the projectors of the cone in all three views. The points 1, 2, 3, 4, 5, 6, 7, can now be projected, beginning at the numbered points in the end view. Remember that each point can be projected as a circuit giving a point in each view. The lines of intersection can now be drawn in the plan and elevation. Draw the development of the cone. The outer generator is true length, and gives the radius for the development arc. A, B, C are chordal lengths from the cone plan. The development of the cylinder should be made in line with its axis. Half the cylinder only is shown.

220. Cone and Cylinder Interpenetration (Second Case) First angle views are given of a large diameter cylinder pierced by a right cone.

Draw the outline of the three views; draw the generators of the cone. Project from the end elevation the intersection points of the cylinder circle and the cone generators, *a, b, c, d*; 1, 2, 3, 4; these will intersect corresponding generators in the front elevation. Join these points to give the two curves of intersection. Project the points to the plan, where the two ellipses can be constructed. The developments of the cone and cylinder can now be attempted, following the same procedure as in 219. Half symmetrical developments are shown.

Construct as a model from the developments as in previous diagrams.

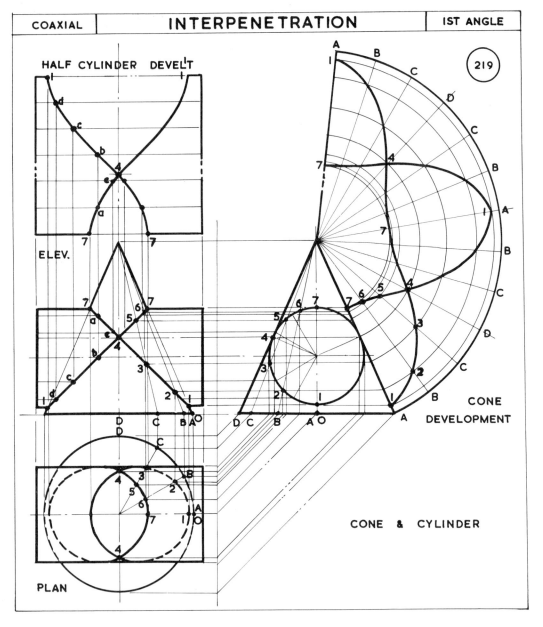

219

HALF CYLINDER DEVEL'T

ELEV.

PLAN

CONE DEVELOPMENT

CONE & CYLINDER

INTERPENETRATION

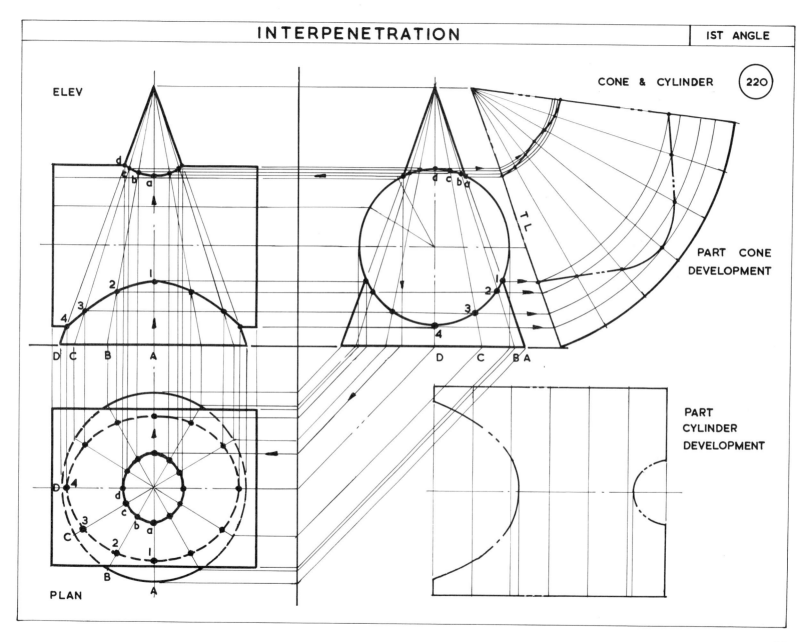

ELEV

CONE & CYLINDER 220

PART CONE
DEVELOPMENT

TL

PART
CYLINDER
DEVELOPMENT

PLAN

221. Cone and Cylinder Interpenetration (Third Case) A large diameter cone is pierced by a small diameter cylinder, shown in third angle projection. Draw the three views; draw the generators of the cone. From the end elevation, project intersection points of cylinder circle and generators, to the front elevation. Draw the line of intersection. Project the points to the plan, and construct the lines of intersection in this view.

The developments of both cone and cylinder may now be constructed by projection in line from the views, adopting the same procedure in the last two diagrams.

222. Sphere and Cylinder Draw the two views as shown. Draw section lines 1, 2, 3, 4, 5, 6, 7, 8, 9; project these to the plan, where they will appear as circles intersecting the cylinder circle, in a, b, c, d, e. Project back to the elevation to intersect the plane lines in a', b', c', d', e'. Draw the line of intersection in the elevation.

Sphere and Cone Draw the given views, Draw section lines 1, 2, 3, 4, 5, 6, 7, 8; project these to the plan where they can be drawn as circles for both sphere and cone. The intersection of the circles in plan gives the curves of intersection; the points may be projected to the elevation to intersect with the plane lines in a', b', c', d', e', f', g', h', through which the curve of intersection may be drawn.

Spherical Ended Cylinder cut by two planes. Draw the two views; draw in the section planes 1, 2, 3, 4, 5, 6, 7; project to the plan where they can be drawn as circles. Where the planes cut the cutting planes points a, b, c, d, e, f, g, are established. Project these to the plan to give the curve of intersection in a', b', c', d', e', f', g'.

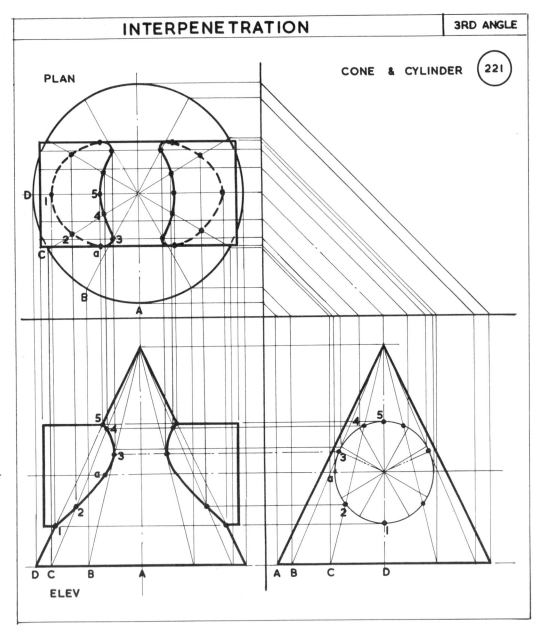

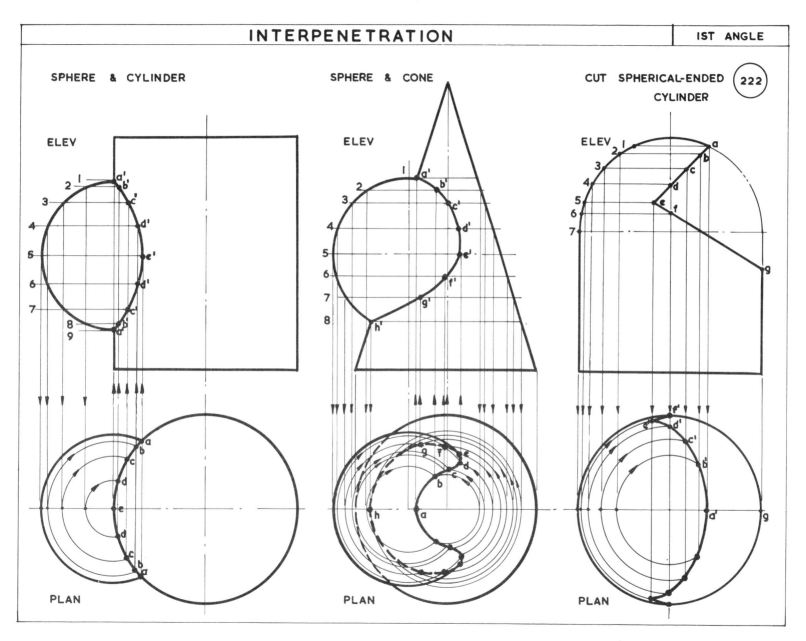

SPHERE & CYLINDER

SPHERE & CONE

CUT SPHERICAL-ENDED CYLINDER

222

ELEV

ELEV

ELEV

PLAN

PLAN

PLAN

223. Composite Interpenetration of cylinder, and cone and cylinder junction. Draw the three first angle projections. Draw cone generators in the places indicated. Where these intersect the cylinder circle in 1, 2, 3, 4, 5, points are given which can be projected to the other views. Radial division lines of the cylinders will give intersection points enabling the curves of intersection to be completed.

The developments may now be drawn, in line with the solids.

The model may be constructed from the developments.

224. A Forged Eye composed of a cylinder and a palmate-ended arm are shown in first angle views.

Draw the outlines of the eye; draw section lines A, B, C, D, in the elevation; project the points to the plan where the planes will appear as arcs. Where the arcs cut the outline in plan, points are made which can be projected back to the section plane in the elevation in points 1, 2, 3, 4, 5. Draw the curve. The end elevation may now be completed.

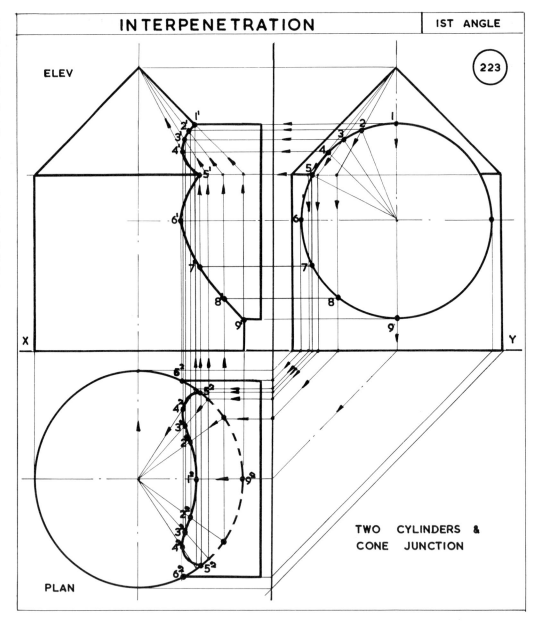

ELEV

X   Y

PLAN

TWO CYLINDERS & CONE JUNCTION

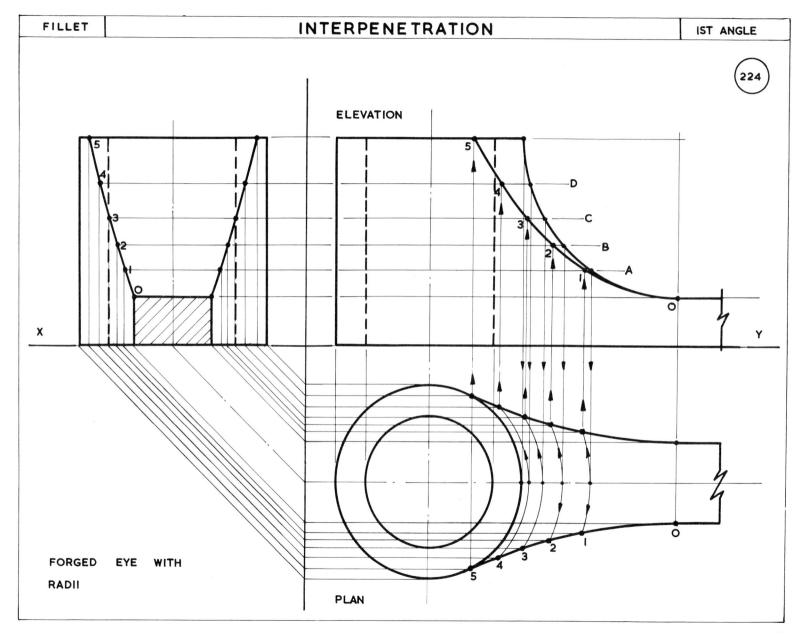

ELEVATION

X   Y

FORGED EYE WITH

RADII

PLAN

224

TWO SECTIONS A & B

PALMATE ROD END

(225)

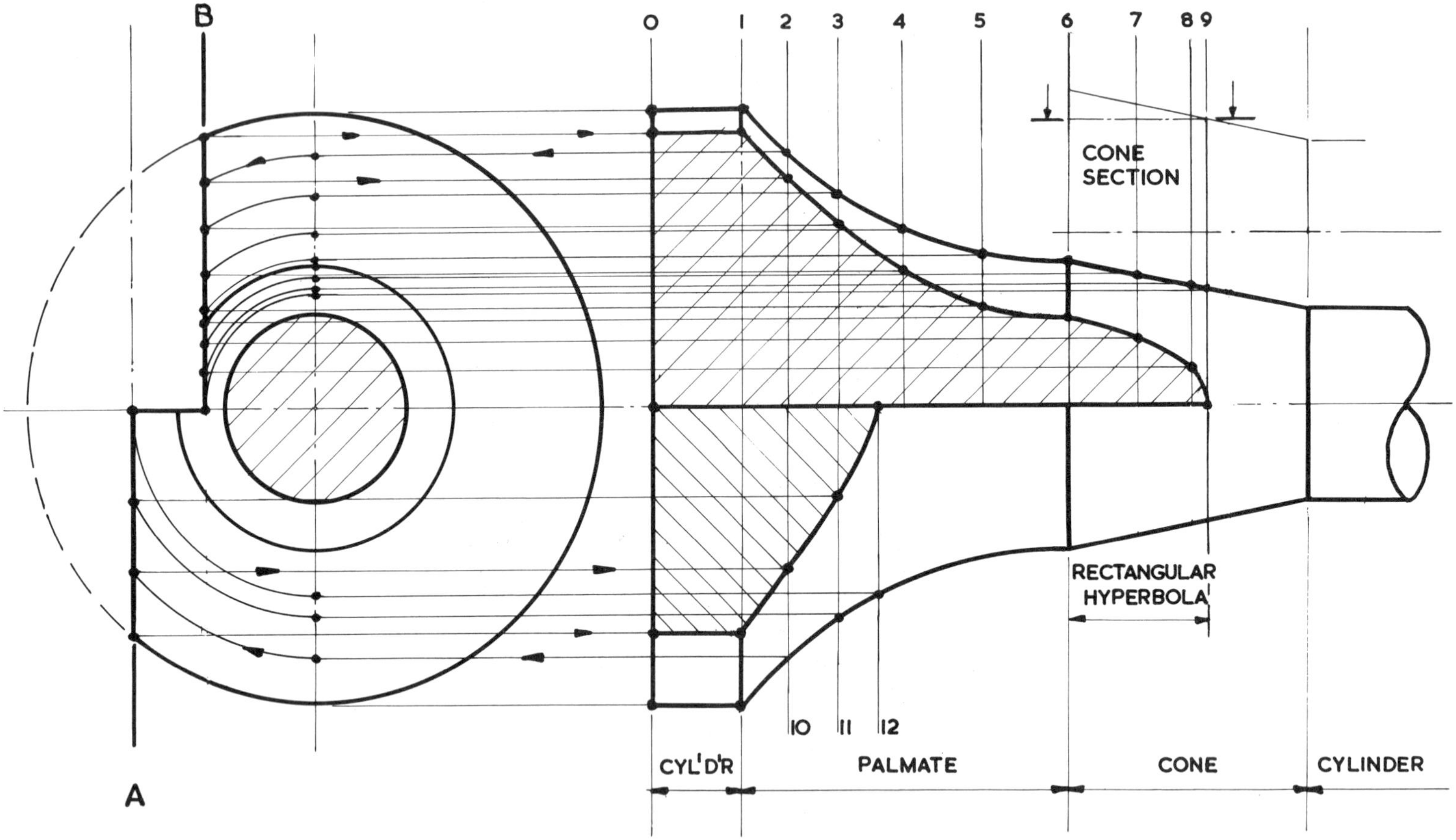

B

0 1 2 3 4 5 6 7 8 9

CONE
SECTION

CONE
SECTION

RECTANGULAR
HYPERBOLA

A

10 11 12

CYL'D'R | PALMATE | CONE | CYLINDER

225. Palmate Rod End Draw the outline of the two views. Draw the two cutting planes A B. Draw the lines of the section planes 1, 2, 3, 4, 5, 6, 7, 8, 9. Project the points where these intersect the outlines of the profile, to the end view, where they are drawn as circles. Project the points where the circles are cut by the planes A and B, back to the respective section plane line. The section face line can now be drawn and the cut face hatched in as shown.

226. Cylinder and Triangular Prism Third angle views are given of the interpenetration. Take the points 1, 2, 3, 4, 5, 6, 7 in the plan, project these in circuit to the end elevation, and thence to the front elevation. Project also from the plan to the front elevation, labelling the points. The curves of intersection can now be drawn.

Developments can be drawn, projected in line with the respective solid.

The model may be constructed from the developments.

227. Solids of Revolution If a lamina is rotated, a solid is generated. A rectangle rotated about one edge, gives a cylinder. A semicircle yields a sphere. A triangle gives a cone. A plane figure rotated will give a solid of symmetrical section. Lathe-turned solids are such symmetrical solids, and a selection is shown. See page 102.

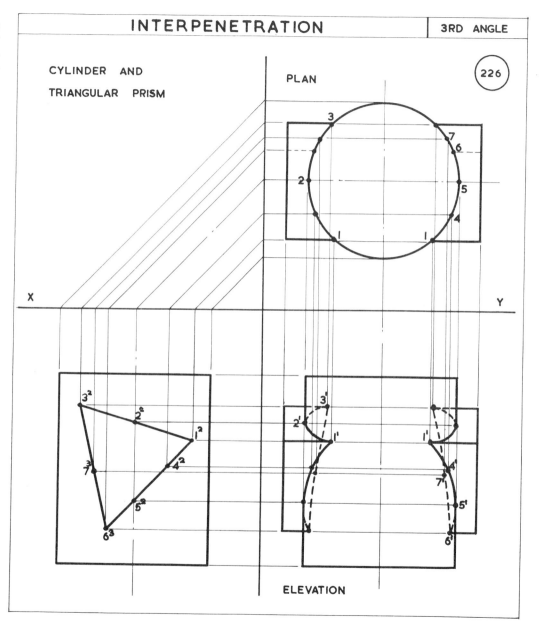

101

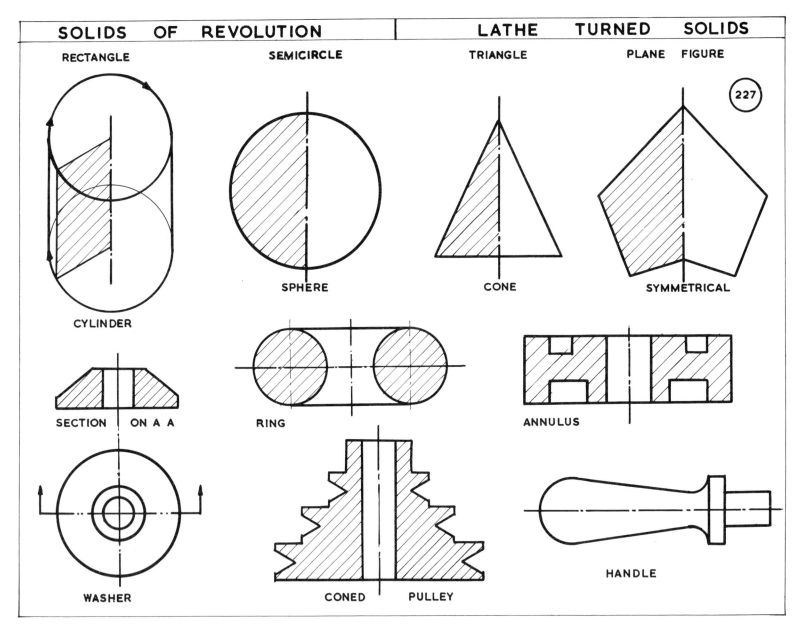

SOLIDS OF REVOLUTION | LATHE TURNED SOLIDS

RECTANGLE   SEMICIRCLE   TRIANGLE   PLANE FIGURE

227

CYLINDER

SPHERE

CONE

SYMMETRICAL

SECTION ON A A

RING

ANNULUS

WASHER

CONED PULLEY

HANDLE

102

PICTORIAL DRAWING

Isometric

Oblique

Freehand

ISOMETRIC PICTORIAL DRAWING

228. Isometric Projection A method of pictorial representation using three planes at 120° to each other as shown in the diagram; these can easily be constructed by the 30° setsquare. Measurements can only be made on the three axes or their parallels. Orthographic first angle views are given of a simple stepped block, and the same block is shown in two typical isometric drawings, from different viewpoints. The object is best enclosed in a box which can easily be drawn in isometric. No diagonal measurements can be made as the two diagonals are not true size. Sizes are taken from the orthographic views and measured directly on the edges of the box. Ordinates are used to obtain points on the faces as shown in the steps.

229. Isometric View of Shaped Block The shaped block is shown in first angle views, and then in isometric. Draw the enclosing box using full sizes from the first angle views given. Points for shaping and slopes have to be measured along the edges of the box, the front face of the block has the same sizes in each case. Notice how the position of the triangular hole is obtained by ordinates-length lines parallel to two of the edges of the box.

230. Pentagonal Prism and Rectangular Prism Draw the boxes first, note the centre line.

231. Octagonal Pyramid First draw the base octagon in its constructional square. From its centre draw the vertical centre line, height as in the ortho. view.

232. Curved Bracket A curved shape may be projected in isometric by first marking suitable points on the curve, and drawing ordinates to the outline box. Draw the box in isometric first; draw the ordinates to the same length and spacing along an axis. Through the points draw the isometric curve.

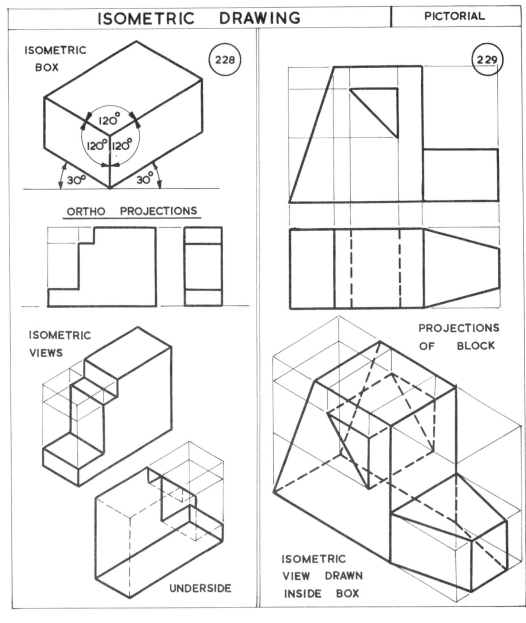

ISOMETRIC DRAWING | PICTORIAL

ISOMETRIC BOX · 228

120° · 120° 120° · 30° · 30°

ORTHO PROJECTIONS

ISOMETRIC VIEWS

UNDERSIDE

229

PROJECTIONS OF BLOCK

ISOMETRIC VIEW DRAWN INSIDE BOX

ISOMETRIC DRAWING

PICTORIAL

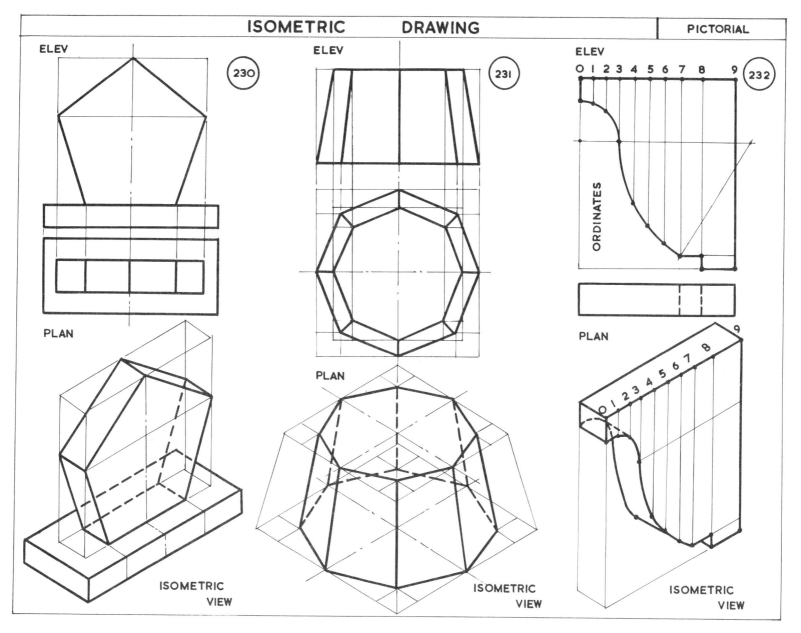

230

ELEV

PLAN

ISOMETRIC
VIEW

231

ELEV

PLAN

ISOMETRIC
VIEW

232

ELEV

O 1 2 3 4 5 6 7 8 9

ORDINATES

PLAN

0 1 2 3 4 5 6 7 8 9

ISOMETRIC
VIEW

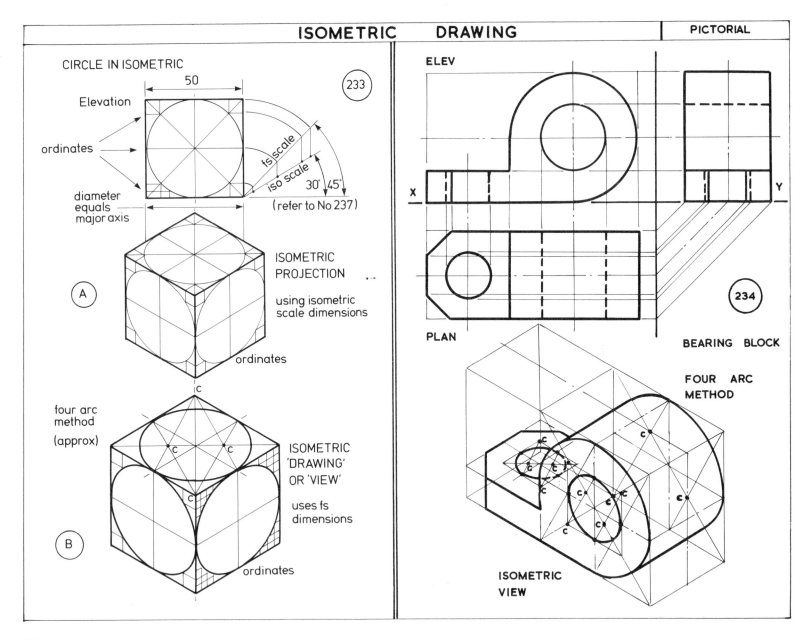

ISOMETRIC DRAWING

CIRCLE IN ISOMETRIC

233

50

Elevation

ordinates

fs scale

iso scale

30° 45°

(refer to No 237)

diameter equals major axis

ISOMETRIC PROJECTION

using isometric scale dimensions

A

ordinates

c

four arc method (approx)

c c

c

ISOMETRIC 'DRAWING' OR 'VIEW'

uses fs dimensions

B

ordinates

ELEV

X   Y

234

PLAN

BEARING BLOCK

FOUR ARC METHOD

ISOMETRIC VIEW

233. The Circle in Isometric A cube has touching circles inscribed on its faces, details as in the elevation. Draw the elevation fs and the Isometric Scale as shown (see 237). Draw the Isometric projection as in diagram A, obtain the points for the ellipse by the ordinate method. Make the Isometric Drawing or View as diagram B but use fs sizes. Construct one ellipse by the four arc method, centres as c. This quick approximate method gives a major axis discrepancy. The grid and ordinate method should always be used unless an examination question allows the arc method. Note how the use of fs sizes in B, the Isometric View, tend to make the object appear larger than the orthographic views suggest.

234. Bearing Block First angle views are given of the bearing block and an isometric view using the four arc method described above. Attempt the exercise two or three times the printed size.

235. The Sphere in Isometric Draw the base block in isometric first, using fs sizes. Now draw a centre vertical line height as the diameter of the sphere. Draw the constructional planes as shown using ordinates to obtain point x. The circle of the envelope of the sphere can now be drawn using c as centre and cx as radius. The diagram shows further how to draw the sphere with a quarter vertical section removed. Part ellipses are drawn on the constructional planes to show the cut faces.

236. The Cone in Isometric Draw the base enclosing square, and the ellipse therein; erect an axis line, and construct the upper enclosing square and the smaller ellipse in it. Draw two tangents to connect the ellipses.

237. Special Isometric Scale Whilst ordinary scale measurements are usually allowed in isometric *drawing*, in isometric *projection* the measurements have to be reduced in the ratio shown in the diagram. This gives a more proportionate diagram. In examination questions when isometric projection is required, it is specially mentioned in the question and a scale must be drawn and the sizes given scaled in the proportion shown.

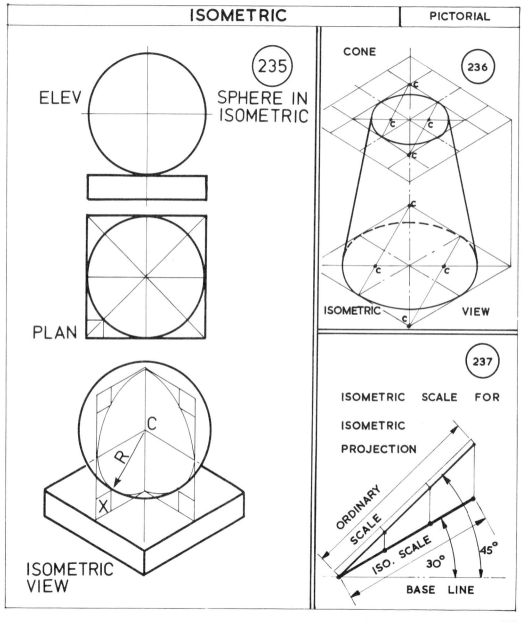

ELEV

235 SPHERE IN ISOMETRIC

PLAN

C

R

X

ISOMETRIC VIEW

CONE 236

ISOMETRIC VIEW

237

ISOMETRIC SCALE FOR

ISOMETRIC PROJECTION

ORDINARY SCALE

ISO. SCALE

45°

30°

BASE LINE

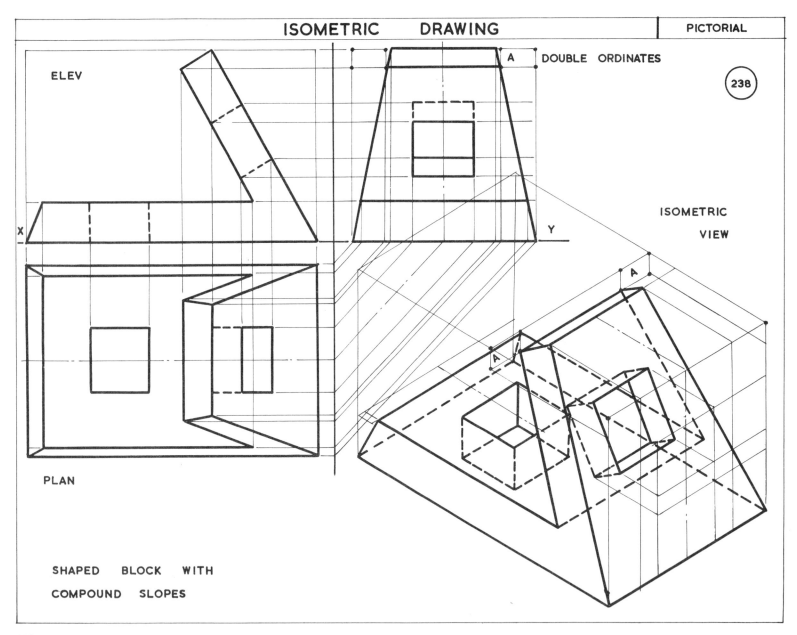

ELEV

DOUBLE   ORDINATES

238

ISOMETRIC

VIEW

X

Y

A

A

A

PLAN

SHAPED   BLOCK   WITH
COMPOUND   SLOPES

238. Shaped Block with Compound Slopes The block shown has compound slopes, and two sets of ordinates will have to be drawn to find the point inside the box, and is shown at A. Trace lines are drawn on the box faces, and secondary projectors from these points into the space of the box. The sloping face and aperture has limits fixed in this way.

239. Isometric View of a Pierced Solid A right square pyramid is pierced by a cylindrical hole as shown. First angle projections are given.

Enclose the plan in a touching square, and draw this in isometric. Centre lines give points enabling the base to be drawn in. Erect the axis to scale height. Join apex to the base to give the outline of the pyramid. Construct the ordinates for a, b, c, d, e, f, g, h, in the isometric view, using sizes from the orthographic end elevation. Ordinates from the plan must now be drawn to intersect projectors a, b, c, etc. This will give points on the curve of intersection; draw in to complete the view.

Whenever a point in the space of the isometric box has to be found, double ordinates must be used as above.

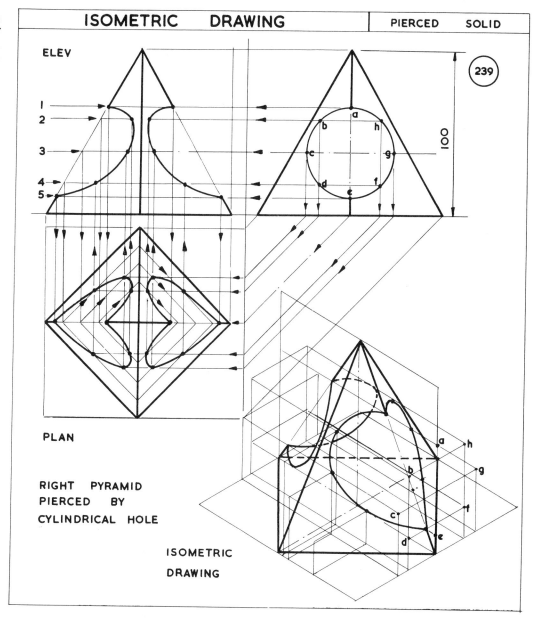

ELEV

239

100

PLAN

RIGHT PYRAMID
PIERCED BY
CYLINDRICAL HOLE

ISOMETRIC

DRAWING

240. Isometric View of a Cylinder pierced by a cylindrical hole. The elevation of the cylinder is given, and the isometric view also. Draw the cylinder first. The four arc method has been used, but the ordinate construction has been used for the hole projection. Note how the ordinates have to be drawn on the face of the enclosing box before projecting to ordinates on the cylinder.

241. Isometric View of a Pierced Hexagonal Prism
Enclose the prism in the box and draw in the usual manner. Ordinates on the end face enable the sloping end and its hole to be drawn. The circular hole is drawn first on the top face by ordinates, and perpendiculars dropped from the points, whose length are the same as in the elevation. The detailed construction is shown.

242. Three Isometric Views
A. **A triangular prism** is pierced by a cylinder. Begin the isometric view with the prism and the axis of the cylinder. Then draw the top and bottom ellipses. Lengths of ordinates from an end elevation will give the points on the line of intersection.
B. The interpenetration of an **hexagonal pyramid** and a hexagonal prism. Draw the pyramid first from the base shape. The prism is drawn from its small hexagon in the base and the vertical axis.
C. **Cone and sphere** Draw the cone first, and its axis. Construct the ellipse at the cone section. Draw the ellipse of the spherical section. Draw the circle of the sphere.

In A, B, C, plan and elevations of the interpenetrations must be drawn first, so that ordinates can be obtained, and their position and length used in the constructions.

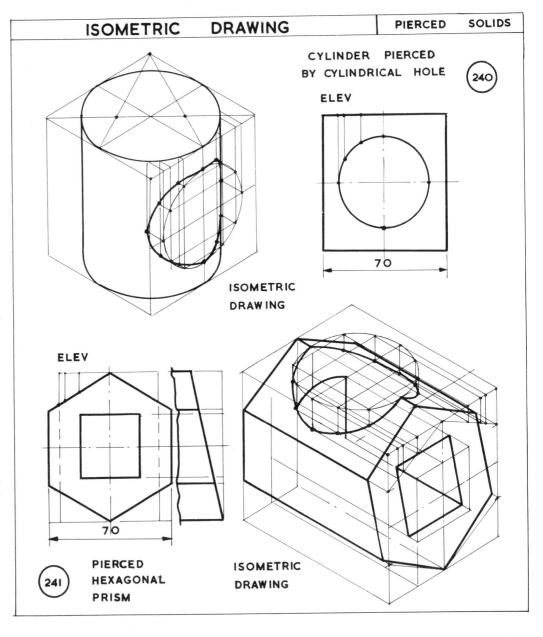

CYLINDER PIERCED BY CYLINDRICAL HOLE — 240

ELEV

70

ISOMETRIC DRAWING

ELEV

70

241 PIERCED HEXAGONAL PRISM

ISOMETRIC DRAWING

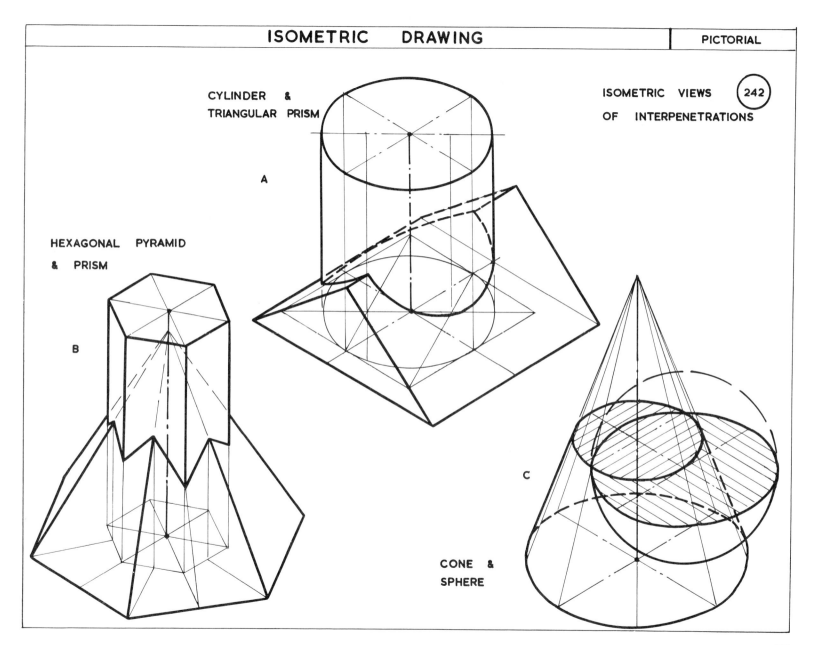

CYLINDER &
TRIANGULAR PRISM

A

ISOMETRIC VIEWS
OF INTERPENETRATIONS

242

HEXAGONAL PYRAMID
& PRISM

B

C

CONE &
SPHERE

243. Oblique Pictorial Projection In this method, the front elevation often forms the front face, and lines are drawn at 45° to give depth. If the depth is full measurement the projection is 'cavalier'. If the depth is shortened, it is 'cabinet'.

A cube is given, showing how the method is used. The depth may be varied to give a more proportionate appearance; also the angle used may be 30° or even 60°.

Prism The method has the advantage that circles in the front face may be drawn with compasses, the centre projected to the rear face and compasses used again in the rear face. The enclosing-box system and ordinates are used for obtaining points on the shape. The prism is also shown in the difficult position, where the circle becomes an ellipse.

Square Pyramid Two views are shown and are self-explanatory.

244. A Cube with Circles on the Faces The compasses can be used for drawing the circle on the front face; an eight-point circle projection gives the ellipse on other sides.

Prisms Two prisms are shown; use the box method in the construction.

Sphere and Base The sphere radius is best enlarged in the proportions shown to give a better appearance.

Bearing Block easy position, using compass curves.

Shaped Block Box construction, easy construction.

Bracket with curves; compasses may be used to draw the curves with the bracket in this position. With the bracket laid in an alternative position, the curves would have to be drawn by the use of ordinates.

When the position of the object to be drawn in oblique parallel projection is not stated, the easiest position should be taken, allowing circles to be drawn quickly and easily with compasses.

Compare the objects drawn on these pages with similar objects drawn in isometric projection, 229 to 234.

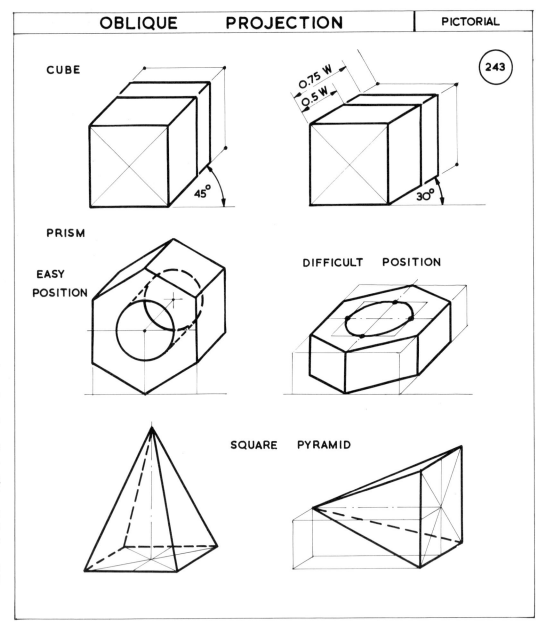

OBLIQUE PROJECTION | PICTORIAL

243

CUBE

0.75 W
0.5 W

45°

30°

PRISM

EASY POSITION

DIFFICULT POSITION

SQUARE PYRAMID

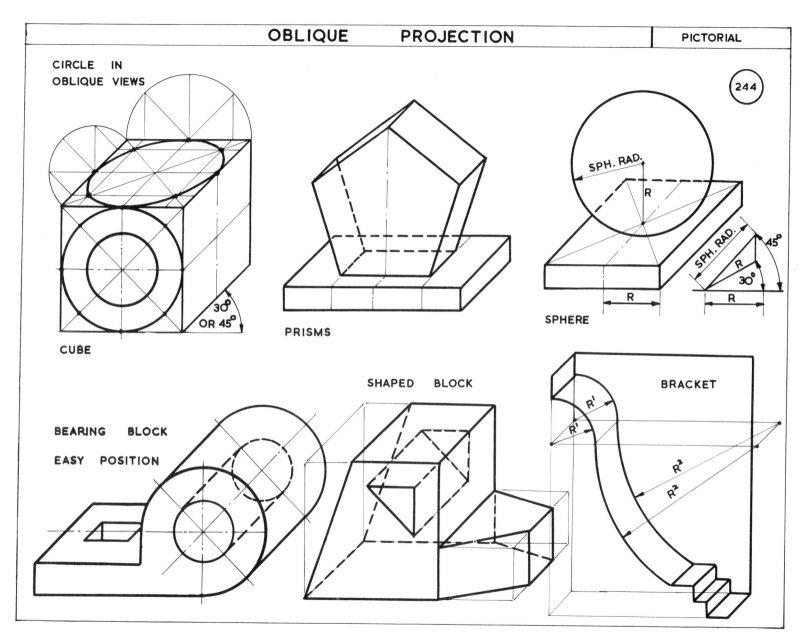

CIRCLE   IN
OBLIQUE   VIEWS

244

30°
OR 45°

CUBE

PRISMS

SPH. RAD.

R

SPH. RAD.

SPH. RAD.

R

45°

R

30°

R

R

SPHERE

SHAPED   BLOCK

BRACKET

BEARING   BLOCK

EASY   POSITION

R^1

R^1

R^1

R^2

R^2

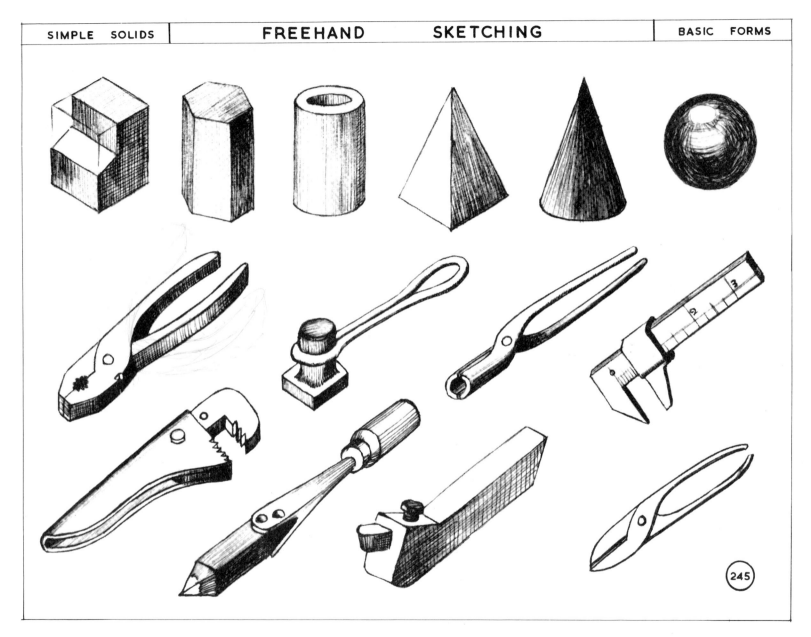

245

245. Freehand Sketching Sketching without instruments should be practised constantly. The simple technique of outline and shading of a sketch based on an isometric or oblique drawing of simple geometric solids should be attempted first. The object is usually illuminated from the left, and shadow shading effected by hatching lines in two directions on plane surfaces. The brightest effect is obtained by placing the deepest shadow adjacent to the highest light.

Analyse the object into its basic geometric solid forms, and sketch boldly to obtain the outline. Pencil shading will give a greater graduation of tone than the pen and ink diagrams shown, HB to 4B pencils can be used. Sketch the solids shown.

Tools are good subjects for sketching; build moving shapes, such as the arms of the pliers, round the pivot rivet.

246. Dimensioned Sketches Sketching of engineering components, nuts, bolts, rivets, bearings, brackets, shafts and housings, and other parts seen in the workshop can be sketched in both isometric and oblique forms. Dimensioned sketches in orthographic form, sectioned and clear, can convey as much as any elaborate blueprint. Workshop sketches are usually made as a preliminary to full orthographic projections, the details being worked out before beginning the time-consuming technical projections.

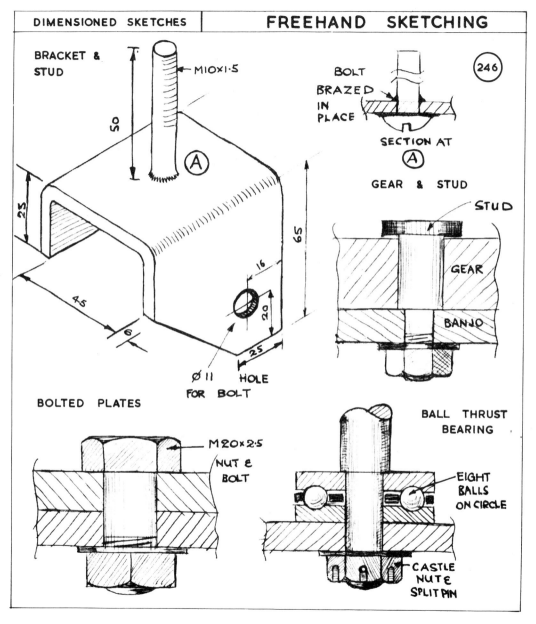

247. A. The first angle elevation of a turned solid is given; project a plan. See 225.

B. The first angle elevation of two intersecting oblique cones is given; find the true lengths required, and draw the developments. See 186.

C. First angle elevation of a turned solid is given. Draw the plan; project the true shape. See 158.

D. Third angle elevation is given of a cone and cylinder. Draw the projections; draw the developments. See 223.

E. Third angle elevation is given of palmate piece. Draw the plan; project the true shape of the section. See 158.

F. Third angle views are given of a forged eye. Complete the projections. See 224.

248. Exercises for Projection Six solids are given suitable for projection in first and third orthographic projection; also for pictorial drawing-isometric, oblique and freehand.

249. Six more exercises for use as above, having more complicated shapes.

250. Six further exercises for projection.

251. Six further exercises for projection.

252. Six exercises for interpenetration.

253. Six further exercises for interpenetration.

254. Six exercises for interpenetration.

255. Solutions. Isometric. 248.

256. Solutions. Isometric. 249.

257. Solutions. Isometric. 250.

258. Solutions. Isometric. 251.

259. Solutions. Isometric. 252.

260. Solutions. Isometric and oblique. 253.

261. Solutions. Isometric. 254.

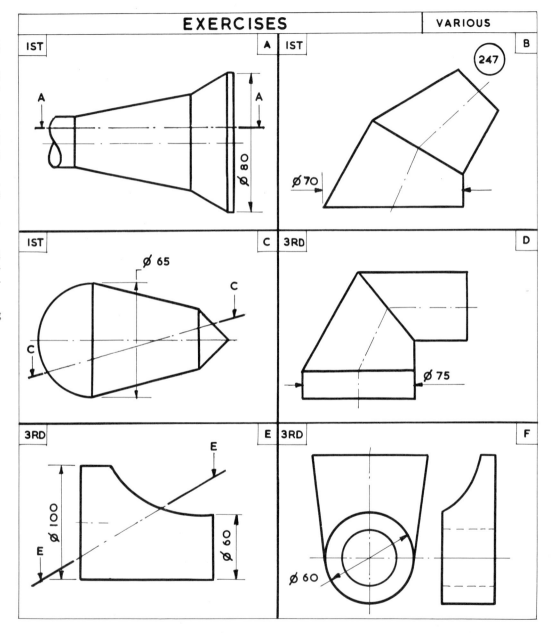

EXERCISES — VARIOUS

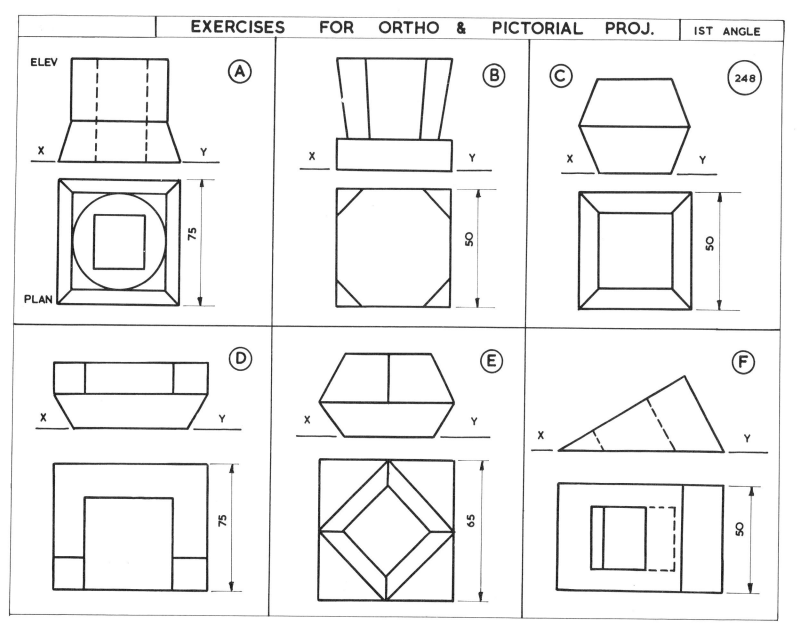

ELEV

X Y

PLAN

75

Ⓐ

Ⓑ

X Y

50

Ⓒ

(248)

X Y

50

Ⓓ

X Y

75

Ⓔ

X Y

65

Ⓕ

X Y

50

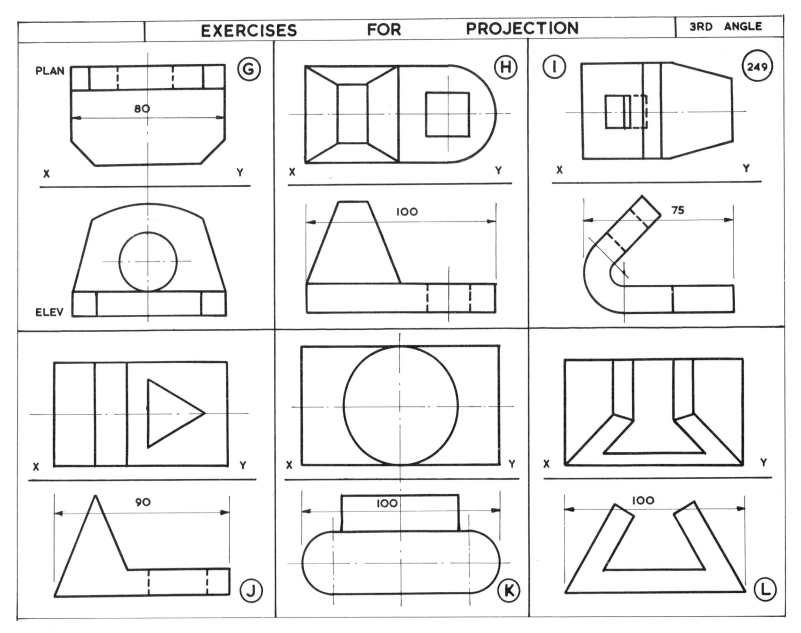

PLAN

G

80

X   Y

ELEV

H

X   Y

100

I   249

X   Y

75

J

90

X   Y

K

100

L

X   Y

100

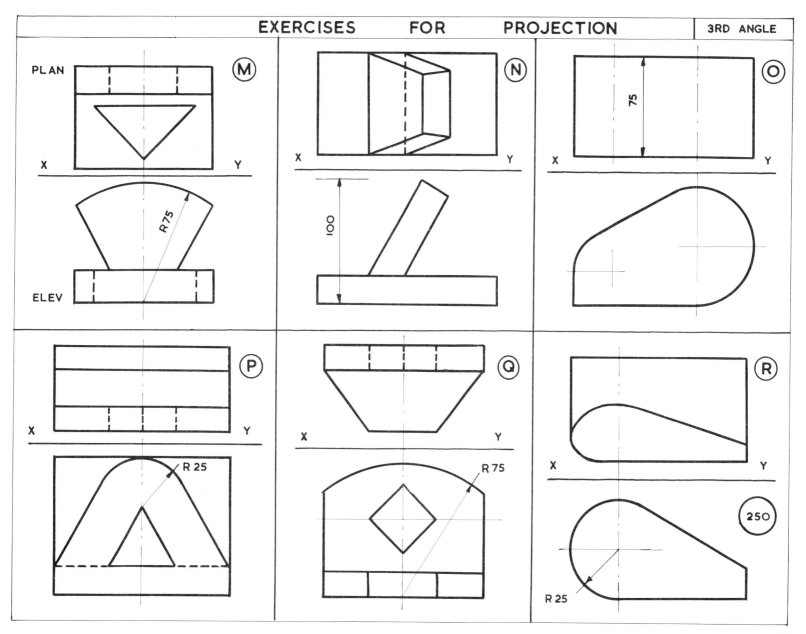

M

PLAN

X — Y

R75

ELEV

N

X — Y

100

O

75

X — Y

P

X — Y

R 25

Q

X — Y

R 75

R

X — Y

R 25

250

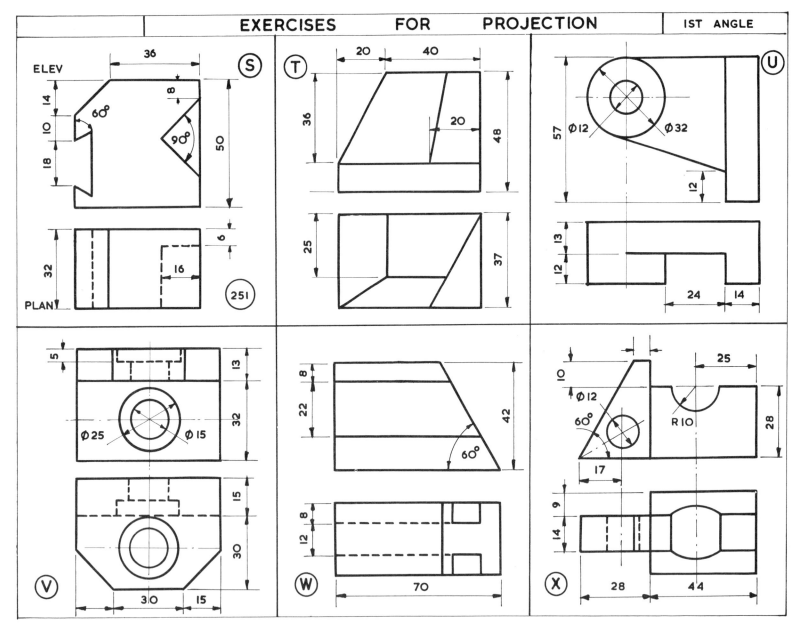

EXERCISES   FOR   PROJECTION   IST ANGLE

S
ELEV
36
14
8
10
60°
18
90°
50
6
32
16
PLAN
251

T
20   40
36
20
48
25
37

U
57
Ø12   Ø32
12
13
12
24   14

V
5
13
32
Ø25   Ø15
15
30
30   15

W
8
22
60°
42
8
12
70

X
10
Ø12
25
60°
R10
28
17
9
14
28   44

120

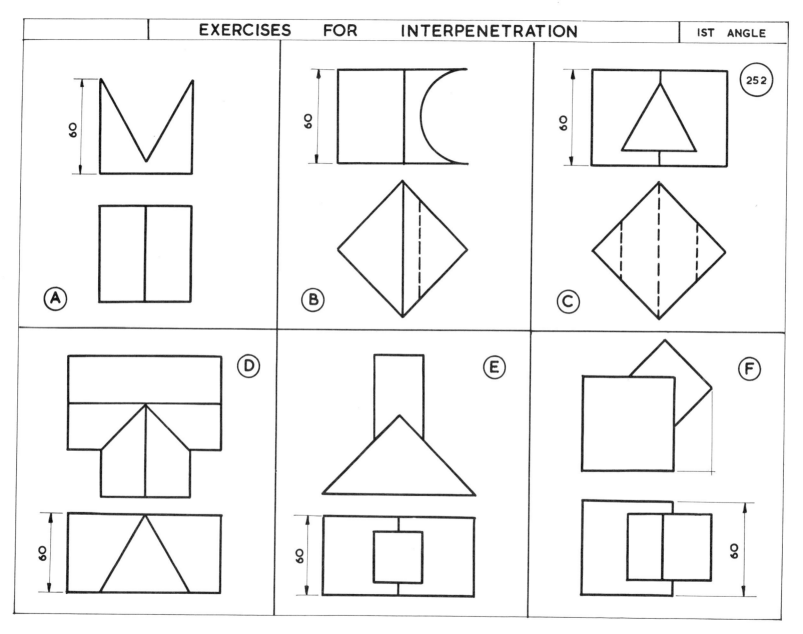

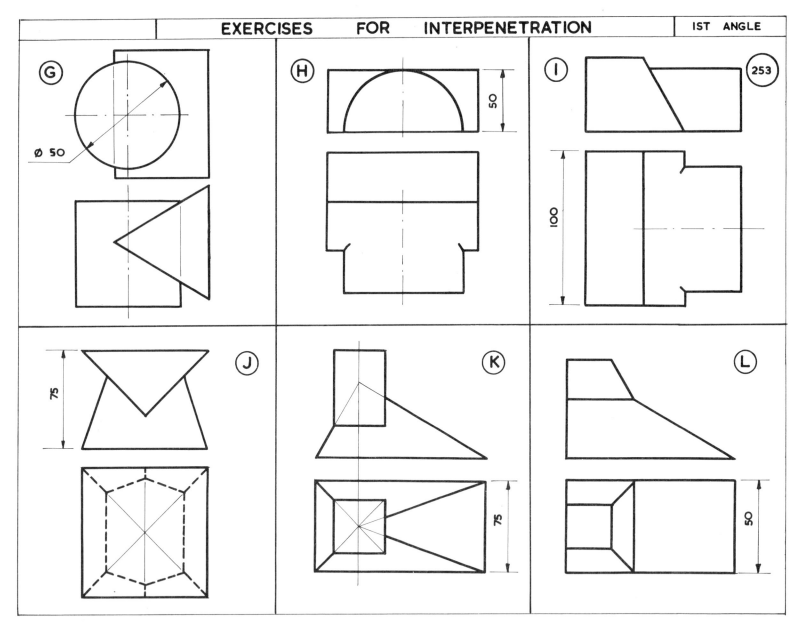

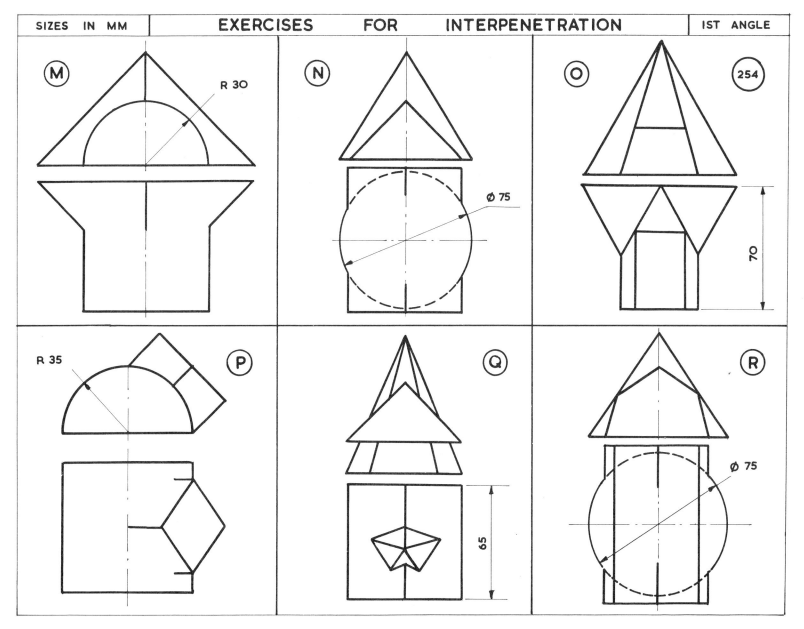

M

R 30

N

Ø 75

O

254

70

R 35

P

Q

65

R

Ø 75

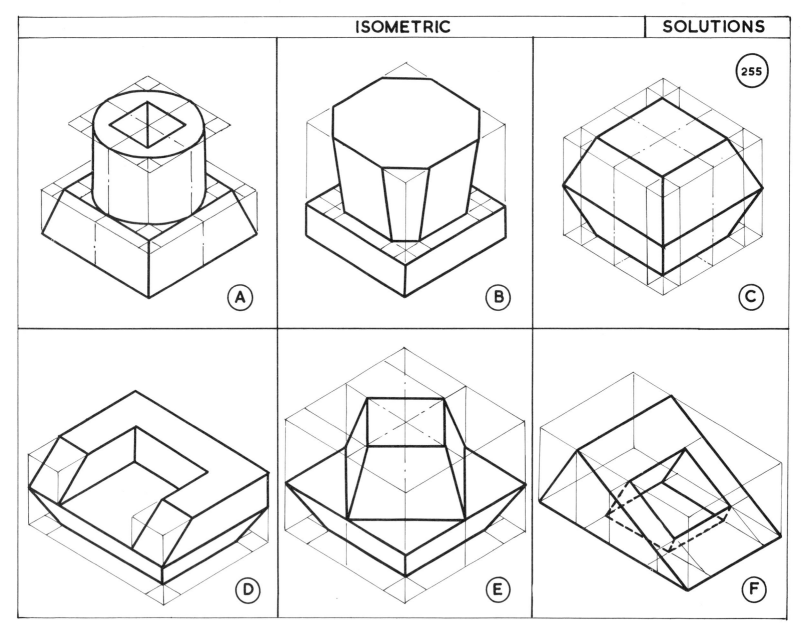

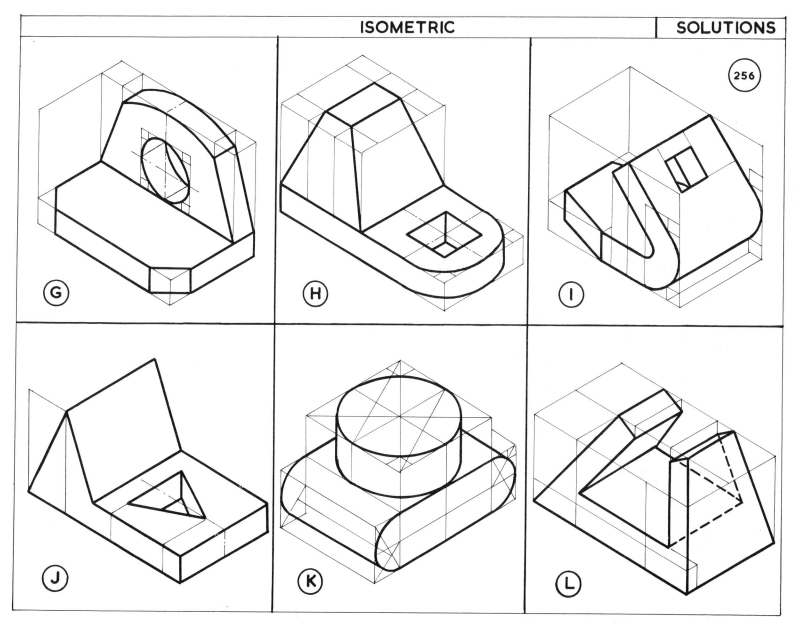

256

G

H

I

J

K

L

125

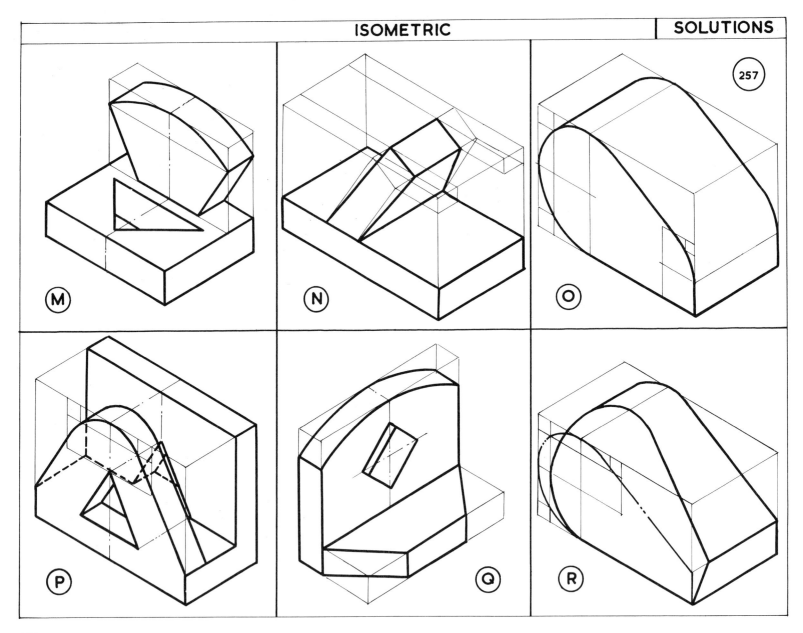

257

M

N

O

P

Q

R

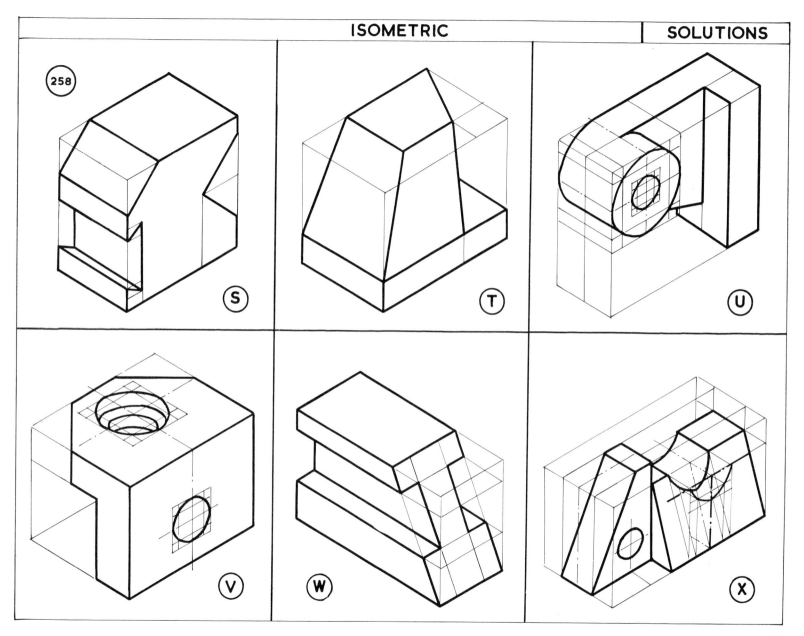

258

S

T

U

V

W

X

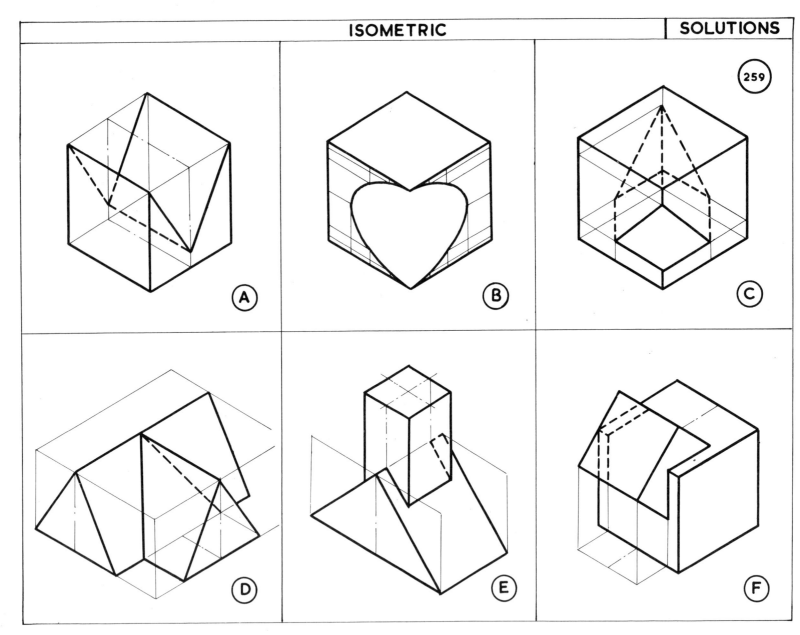

259

A

B

C

D

E

F

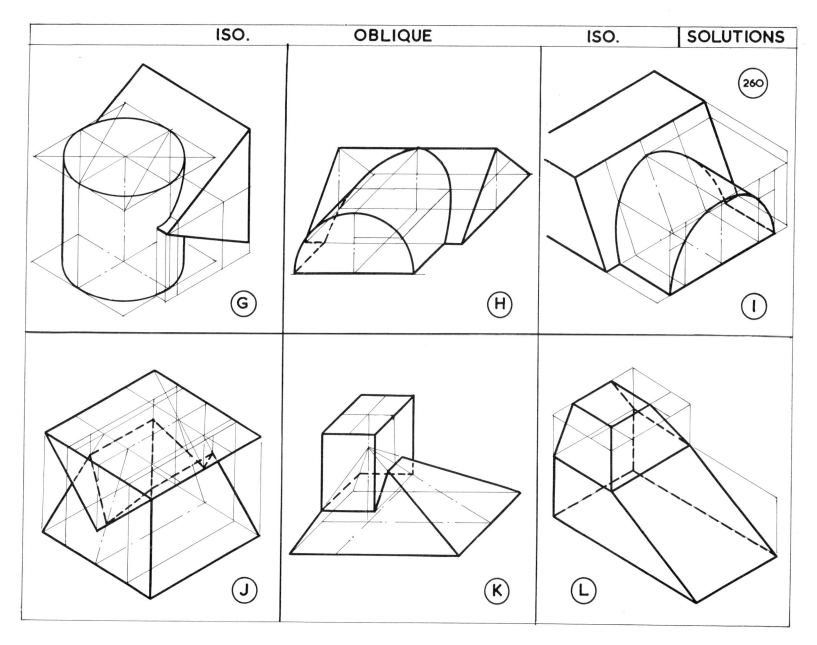

260

G

H

I

J

K

L

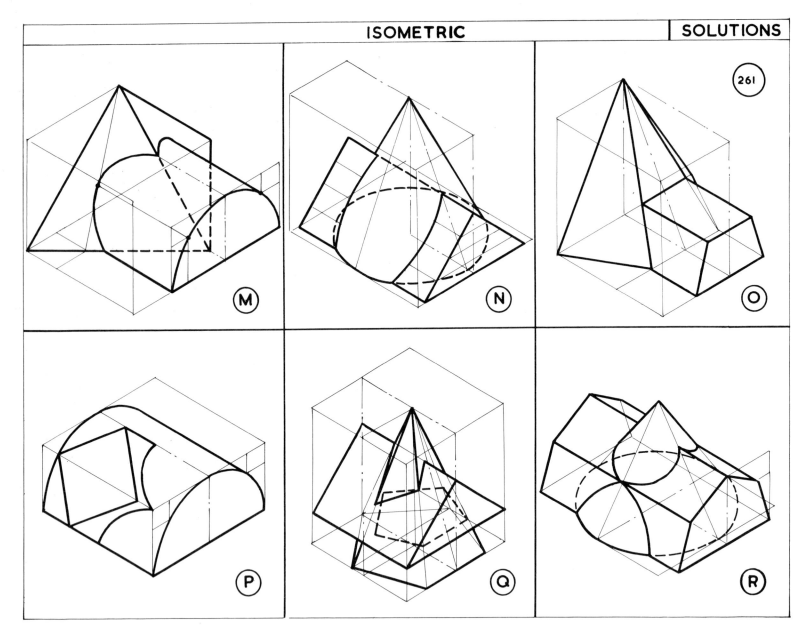

Part II

ENGINEERING DRAWING

Standards

Conventions

Fastenings

Components

MACHINE DRAWING

Assemblies

Parts

STANDARDS & CONVENTIONS

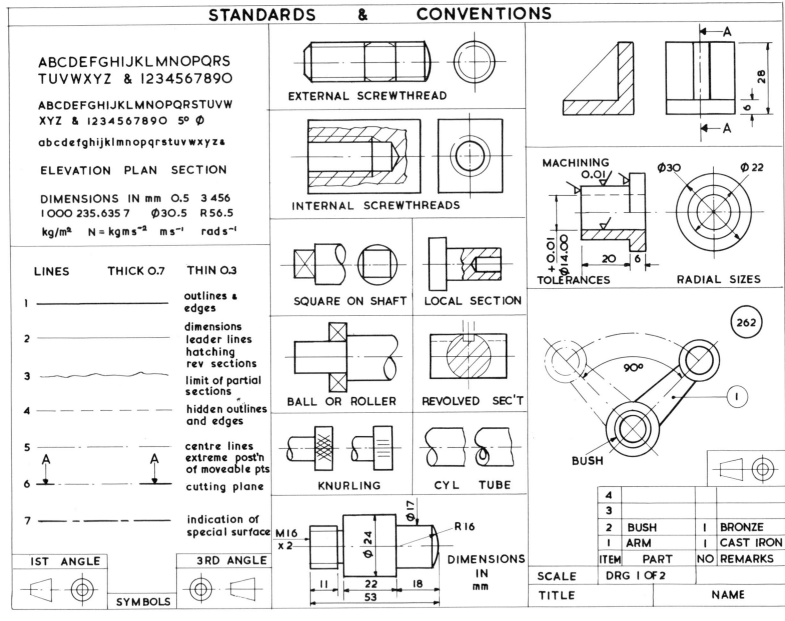

ABCDEFGHIJKLMNOPQRS
TUVWXYZ & 1234567890

ABCDEFGHIJKLMNOPQRSTUVW
XYZ & 1234567890 5° Ø

abcdefghijklmnopqrstuvwxyz&

ELEVATION PLAN SECTION

DIMENSIONS IN mm 0.5 3 456
1 000 235.635 7   Ø30.5 R56.5
kg/m² N = kgms⁻² ms⁻¹ rads⁻¹

LINES   THICK 0.7   THIN 0.3

1   outlines & edges
2   dimensions leader lines hatching rev sections
3   limit of partial sections
4   hidden outlines and edges
5   centre lines extreme post'n of moveable pts
6   cutting plane
7   indication of special surface

1ST ANGLE   3RD ANGLE

SYMBOLS

EXTERNAL SCREWTHREAD

INTERNAL SCREWTHREADS

SQUARE ON SHAFT   LOCAL SECTION

BALL OR ROLLER   REVOLVED SEC'T

KNURLING   CYL TUBE

M16 x 2   Ø24   Ø17   R 16
11   22   18
53
DIMENSIONS IN mm

28
6

MACHINING 0.01   Ø30   Ø22
Ø14.00 +0.01 0.01   20   6
TOLERANCES   RADIAL SIZES

262
90°
1
BUSH

4			
3			
2	BUSH	1	BRONZE
1	ARM	1	CAST IRON
ITEM	PART	NO	REMARKS
SCALE	DRG 1 OF 2		
TITLE		NAME	

132

262. Standards The British Standard 308: 1972 parts 1, 2, 3 covers fully the conventional methods of representing engineering components in drawing practice and is the recommended reference book for most examinations. It may be necessary to refer to the standard for fuller explanation on difficult points, as many items are discussed in more detail than is possible in this volume.

A simple sans-serif block lettering, figures, and seven types of drawing lines are shown, and their special uses are shown in later drawings. A selection of frequently used symbols is shown; a method of sectioning by hatching; dimensioning; and a drawing layout are also shown.

263. Conventions Selection of items used.

A. The method of showing a drilled countersunk hole in a plate. Two dimensions giving location, instruction of sizes.
B. Sectional view of a hole, detailed instructions. Counterboring and countersinking.
C. Drilled hole with spot facing enabling bolthead to sit truly.
D. Conventional quickly drawn screwthread. Depth; clearance; amount of thread length; diameter and pitch; type of screwthread; quality of machining. (Metric threads are given in the tables in the appendix.)
E. Method of showing a tapered shaft, with tolerances.
F. Toleranced sizes of hole and shaft to give type of fit required.

Tolerances and Limits Running fits between shafts and bushes may be required to be machined to certain limits stated on the drawing, and error beyond these limits not tolerated. A shaft and bush are shown dimensioned to such limits and tolerances as a typical example.

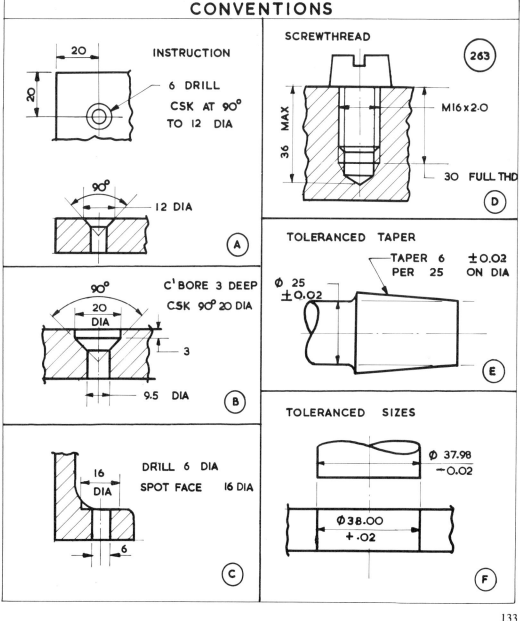

CONVENTIONS

INSTRUCTION

6 DRILL
CSK AT 90°
TO 12 DIA

12 DIA

A

C'BORE 3 DEEP
CSK 90° 20 DIA

9.5 DIA

B

DRILL 6 DIA
SPOT FACE 16 DIA

C

SCREWTHREAD

263

M16 x 2·0

30 FULL THD

D

TOLERANCED TAPER

TAPER 6 ±0.02
PER 25 ON DIA

Ø 25 ±0.02

E

TOLERANCED SIZES

Ø 37.98 −0.02

Ø38.00 +·02

F

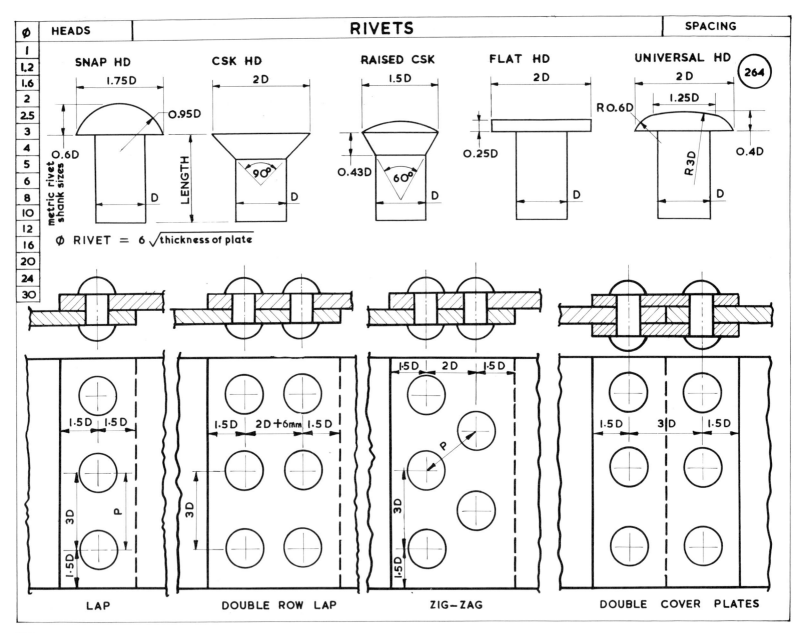

RIVETS

HEADS | **SPACING** | 264

metric rivet shank sizes: 1, 1.2, 1.6, 2, 2.5, 3, 4, 5, 6, 8, 10, 12, 16, 20, 24, 30

SNAP HD — 1.75D, 0.95D, 0.6D, D

CSK HD — 2D, 90°, LENGTH, D

RAISED CSK — 1.5D, 0.43D, 60°, D

FLAT HD — 2D, 0.25D, D

UNIVERSAL HD — 2D, 1.25D, R 0.6D, R 3D, 0.4D, D

$\varnothing \ \text{RIVET} = 6\sqrt{\text{thickness of plate}}$

LAP — 1.5D | 1.5D, 3D, P, 1.5D

DOUBLE ROW LAP — 1.5D | 2D+6mm | 1.5D, 3D

ZIG-ZAG — 1.5D | 2D | 1.5D, P, 3D, 1.5D

DOUBLE COVER PLATES — 1.5D | 3D | 1.5D

134

Fastenings

264. Rivets A rivet is classed as a permanent method of metal fastening. The ordinary rivet is supplied with one head stamped to shape, the second head is burred by the hammer after insertion. A number of different heads are shown to suit the requirements of the work.

Details are given of five recommended ISO rivet heads for general use with proportions stated in terms of D the diameter of the shank of the rivet. This rivet diameter can be obtained by applying the formulae shown when the plate thickness is given.

Types of Riveted Joints.

Simple Lap simple overlap of the two ends of plate to be joined. Spacing and pitch as shown to prevent tearing and shear.

Double Row Lap Joint Two rows of rivets spaced as shown.

Double Row Zig-Zag Spacing as shown.

Double Cover Plates Two rows of rivets with cover plates. Cover plates may also use zig-zag and double riveting.

265. Riveted Constructions Various types of corner joints, box forms, and a gusset plate cross-joint.

266. Special Rivets for thin plates. Tubular; Pop mushroom; Explosive for inaccessible places; Dimpled to give flush, level finish.

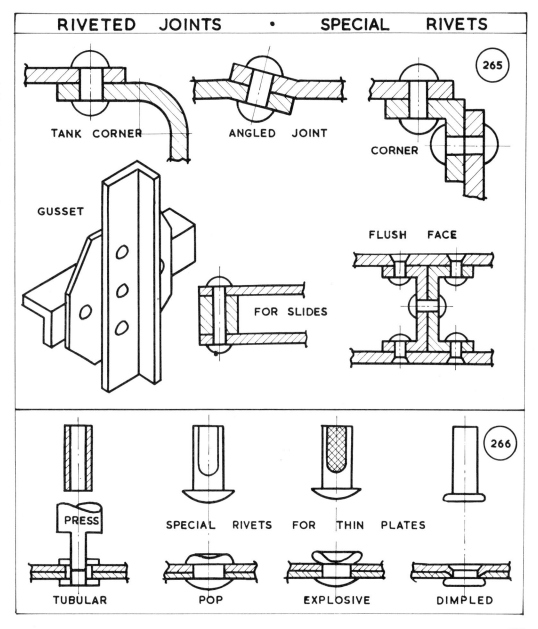

RIVETED JOINTS • SPECIAL RIVETS

TANK CORNER

ANGLED JOINT

CORNER

GUSSET

FOR SLIDES

FLUSH FACE

265

PRESS

SPECIAL RIVETS FOR THIN PLATES

TUBULAR

POP

EXPLOSIVE

DIMPLED

266

267. ISO Bolts Nuts and Washers The conventional methods of drawing the metric screw fastenings are shown with proportions in terms of D = shank diameter. The head may be drawn using a constructional circle 2D in diameter, enclosing the hexagon, or alternatively, the chamfer circle may be drawn first 1·75D in diameter, and enclosing it with the hexagon.

The conventional method of rendering external screwthreads on bolt and stud is shown, note the use of thick and thin lines to indicate overall dimension and thread line.

Internal screwthreads require hatching to extend over the threaded portion.

Screwthreads assembly shows the bolt clear and the internal threads hatched over.

Thread inserts are shown in clear lines.

The designation of ISO bolts requires: material, head shape, thread diameter, pitch, length, type of fit.

Example: Steel, Hex Hd Bolts,
M $10 \times 1·5 \times 50 - 6g$
Steel, Hex Nuts,
M $10 \times 1·5 - 6H$

Types of fit for bolts are:
close fit, 4h; medium fit, 6g,
free fit, 8g.

Types of fit for nuts are:
close fit 5H, medium 6H
free fit, 7H.

See Appendix 1 for tables.

BS 308 1972 part 1.
BS 1936 ISO Metric screwthreads.
BS Handbook No. 18.

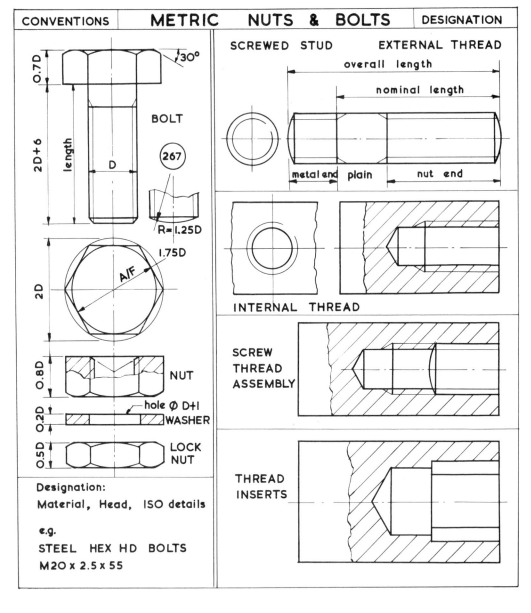

CONVENTIONS | METRIC NUTS & BOLTS | DESIGNATION

BOLT

NUT

WASHER

LOCK NUT

Designation:
Material, Head, ISO details

e.g.
STEEL HEX HD BOLTS
M20 x 2.5 x 55

SCREWED STUD   EXTERNAL THREAD

INTERNAL THREAD

SCREW THREAD ASSEMBLY

THREAD INSERTS

268. Screw Fastenings The conventional method of showing a nut and bolt assembly is given using a washer to facilitate the final tightening of the nut.

The two other diagrams show methods using a screwed stud or alternatively a set bolt for fixing a lighter component to a heavier base which allows the boring of deep blind holes.

Square Threads Used for threads mostly in machines which have to take continuous pressure movement in both clockwise and anti-clockwise direction. Machine slides are often operated by square thread screwthreads.

Acme Threads Chiefly used for lead screws on lathes.

Buttress Threads Used where the pressure is chiefly in one direction, as in quick release vices and slides; a half-nut disengages on the return.

Metric Thread A 60° angle thread similar to the American Sellers thread, sizes in millimetres. See ISO Metric Threads in the appendix. Fine and coarse forms. Instruction could read; M6 × 0·75, which would indicate a metric thread 6 mm in diam., with a pitch of $\frac{3}{4}$ mm.

The thread of a screw follows the path of a helical groove cut or rolled on the cylinder of the bolt or stud, and may be right or lefthanded, single or multistart, see helices (131–134). The pitch is measured from crest to crest of two adjacent thread forms. The major diameter is the full diameter over the crests. The minor diameter is the core or root diameter. All threads may be conventionally represented by the method in 267, with printed instruction of type of thread used.

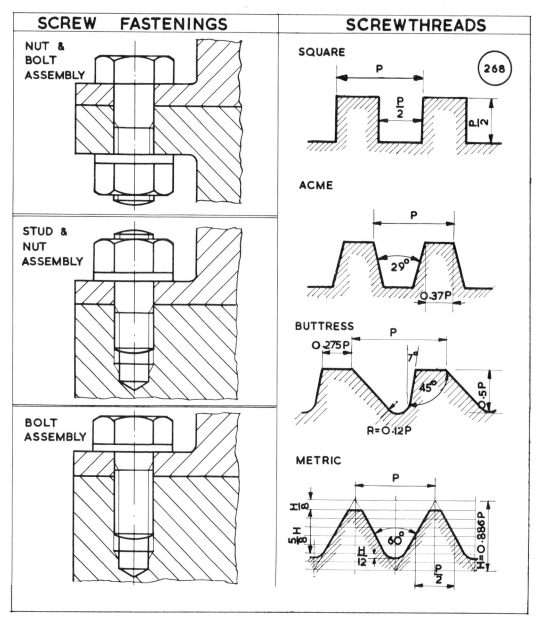

SCREW FASTENINGS

NUT & BOLT ASSEMBLY

STUD & NUT ASSEMBLY

BOLT ASSEMBLY

SCREWTHREADS

SQUARE

ACME

BUTTRESS

METRIC

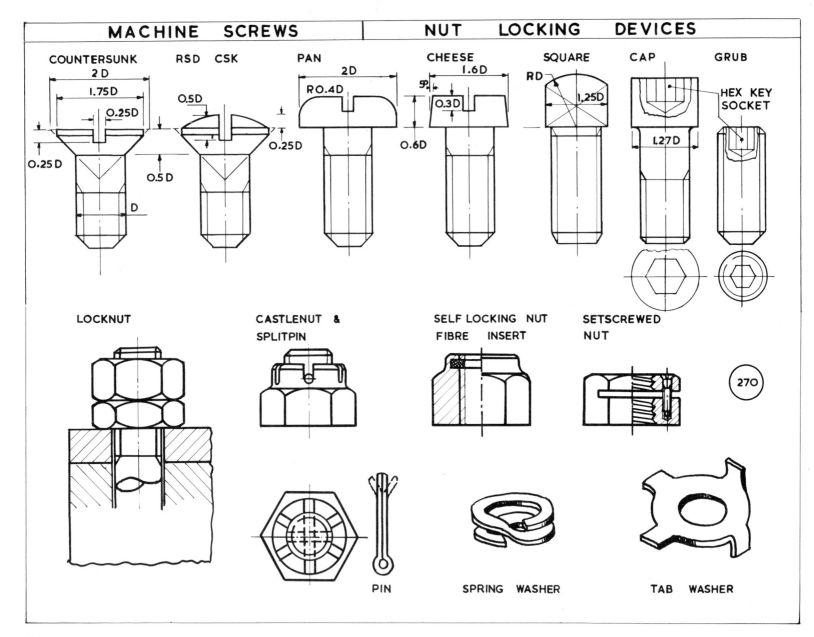

COUNTERSUNK
2D
1.75D
0.25D
0.25D
D

RSD CSK
0.5D
0.25D
0.5D

PAN
2D
RO.4D

CHEESE
1.6D
5°
0.3D
0.6D

SQUARE
RD
1.25D

CAP
1.27D

GRUB
HEX KEY SOCKET

LOCKNUT

CASTLENUT & SPLITPIN

SELF LOCKING NUT FIBRE INSERT

SETSCREWED NUT

270

PIN

SPRING WASHER

TAB WASHER

269. ISO Machine Screws Stock machine screws take the form shown, the proportions are given in terms of the shank diameter D.

Pan and **Cheese Head** screws are used for general work.

Countersunk and **raised countersunk** are used for flush finished surfaces or situations allowing slight raising respectively.

Square Head screws are tightened by spanner, and are used in situations where vibration is present, flywheels and pulleys.

Cap Screws are used either as ordinary fastenings or set in suitable shaped countersinks to give a flush finish. The hexagonal socket allows strong tightening by suitable hexagonal key.

Grubscrews are either slotted or hexagonal socketed for keys and are used where a flush finish is required.

Some screwheads may be recessed or closed slotted for use with a special screwdriver.

270. Nut Locking Devices Vibration causes nuts to work loose with disastrous results in high speed machinery. Locking devices such as **Locknuts**; a second nut tightened against the first; **Castlenut** and split pin, enabling the nut to be tightened and the pin inserted at that position; **Self-locking Nuts**, having a fibre or nylon ring insert; a **Setscrewed Nut**, the cut being closed after tightening; **Spring and Tab Washers** which prevent rotation.

271. Keys and Keyways Keys are used to fix shafts and wheels or collars together, either rigidly or with limited axial movement.

Rectangular Key, Round Pin, Feather, Woodruff and **Taper Gib** are types of keys in general use.

272. Cotters This fixing device may be a

Taper Pin, fitting in a tapered reamed hole driven in to fix a collar or wheel; or a

Split Pin, inserted and ends opened out.

Gib and Cotter, a tapered rectangular sectioned flat cotter pin driven in with a gib piece also tapered.

Simple Taper Cotter, wedged, shaped flat cotter driven in slots for drawing two pieces—spigot and taper socket—together rigidly.

Split Tapered Cotters a locking, tapered cotter in two halves, fitting a matching tapered collar.

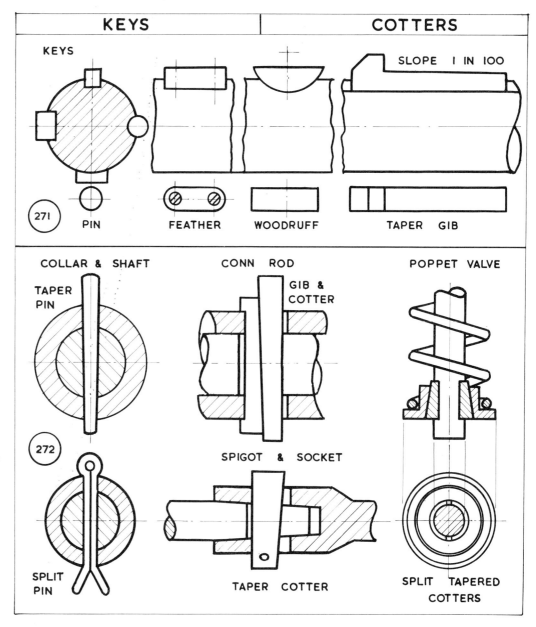

KEYS   COTTERS

KEYS

PIN   FEATHER   WOODRUFF   TAPER GIB

SLOPE 1 IN 100

271

COLLAR & SHAFT   CONN ROD   POPPET VALVE

TAPER PIN

GIB & COTTER

272

SPLIT PIN

SPIGOT & SOCKET

TAPER COTTER

SPLIT TAPERED COTTERS

273. Mechanical Movements Sliding Movements in machines may be made by the use of **Splined Shafts** and **Collars** which allow the collar to remain enmeshed with the shaft whilst being moved laterally. Used in gear-boxes for disengaging and re-engaging geared shafts. See 143.

Lathe and Milling Machine Slides are usually made dovetail in section, and fitted with a gib strip. The setscrews are locknutted.

Lathe Gear Banjo A casting having two or more slotted arms, enabling a train of gearwheels to be set up (usually for screw-cutting).

Adjustable Radial Arm An arm which carries two or more shafts, allowing the arm to be clamped at the desired angle, enabling gears to mesh.

274. Bearings Steel shafts usually turn in bearings lined with another metal, such as brass, bronze or white metal for anti-friction purposes. Bearings may be **plain** or made in two **matching halves** to allow replacement or adjustment.

Ball Race Bearings Friction may be greatly reduced by the use of a ring of balls giving only point contact and lessening bearing friction.

Taper Roller Bearings Rollers may be used instead of balls and capable of bearing greater loads. Plain roller bearings are much used, but the example shows a taper roller bearing which is capable of withstanding thrust and pressure from several directions. Used extensively on automobile road wheels.

275. Compressor Unit Used for pumping gases or liquids under pressure. The cylinder is finned to allow air cooling to dissipate the heat generated. Two non-return valves are used; one allowing gas or liquid to be drawn in on the charging stroke, the other allowing discharge to be made on the delivery stroke. Ball valves are shown but often disc flap valves are used.

276. Lubrication Points Machinery requires a film of oil or grease between moving parts to prevent the parts from seizing up. The bearing surfaces can be fed by drip, by pressure pump, by greasing under pressure by hose or screwdown cups.

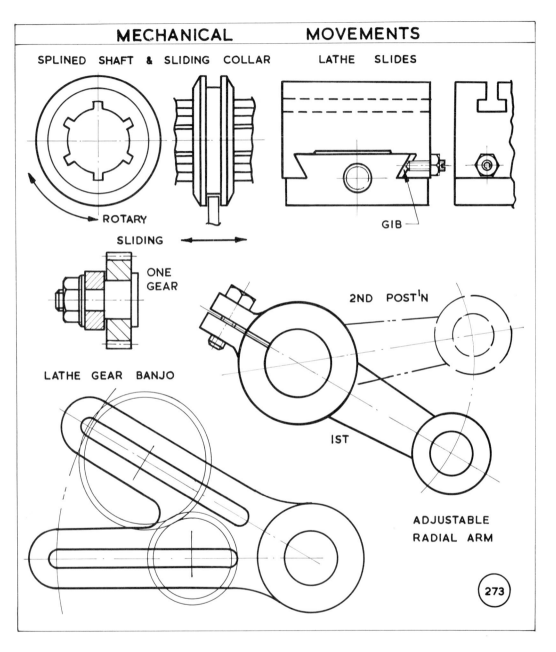

MECHANICAL MOVEMENTS

SPLINED SHAFT & SLIDING COLLAR

LATHE SLIDES

ROTARY

SLIDING

GIB

ONE GEAR

LATHE GEAR BANJO

2ND POST'N

1ST

ADJUSTABLE RADIAL ARM

273

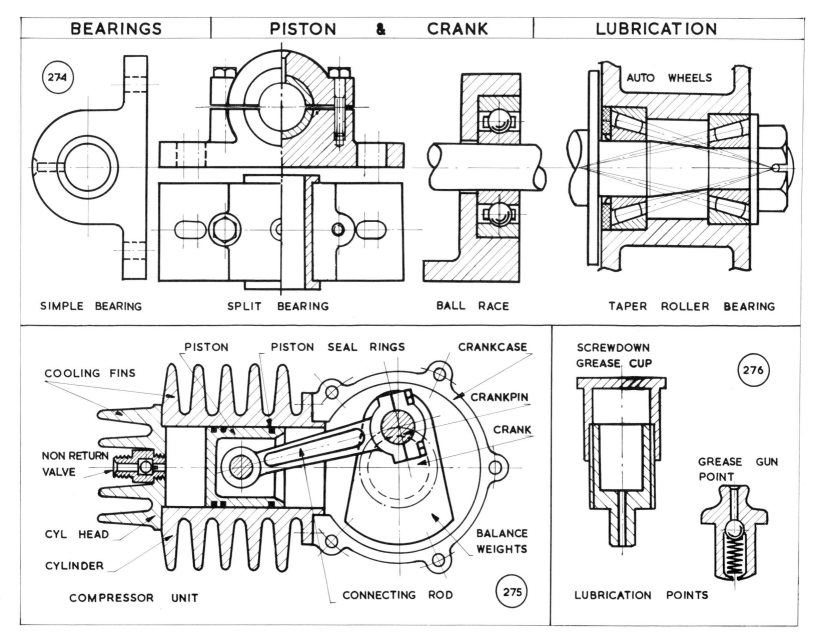

274

SIMPLE BEARING

SPLIT BEARING

BALL RACE

AUTO WHEELS

TAPER ROLLER BEARING

PISTON   PISTON SEAL RINGS   CRANKCASE

COOLING FINS

CRANKPIN

CRANK

NON RETURN
VALVE

CYL HEAD

CYLINDER

BALANCE
WEIGHTS

COMPRESSOR UNIT

CONNECTING ROD

275

SCREWDOWN
GREASE CUP

276

GREASE GUN
POINT

LUBRICATION POINTS

141

277. Shaft U Seal Shafts and pump rams often require high pressure sealing against leakage. This is accomplished by a sealing ring forced against both shaft and housing. Early types of seals, leather, braided hemp, cotton, flax have largely been superseded by synthetic rubber, butyl, silicone, nylon and other plastics. In this example, a U shaped section seal is held in place by an adjustable gland plate bolted to the housing.

278. Garter Seal The seal is compressed on the shaft by a garter spring ring.

279. Flexible Coupling To avoid having unwieldy lengths of shaft, couplings are made between lengths or to attach a driving unit. In the example, an end plate is keyed to the ends of each shaft, and bolted in between is a plate consisting of rubber bonded to a metal plate. This allows a slight flexible movement to take place, angled and radially, and also torsionally, cushioning the drive.

280. Cone Clutch Where two shafts have to be disengaged and re-engaged, a clutch such as the diagram shows may be used. The hollow cone is fixed firmly to the shaft to be driven; the second mating conical end is attached to the second shaft.

281. Flanged Pipe Coupling Much modern engineering is devoted to the conveyance of gases and liquids under pressure in pipe systems.

282. Stop Valve Screw-down stop valves are used for reducing or stopping a piped supply.

283. Safety Release Valve A spring-loaded ball valve automatically releases the excess pressure. The valve is pre-set to lift at the required pressure per square inch.

284. Non-Return Mushroom Valve Where a one-way flow is required, non-return valves must be included in the system.

285. Ball Non-Return Valve A simple ball non-return valve is shown.

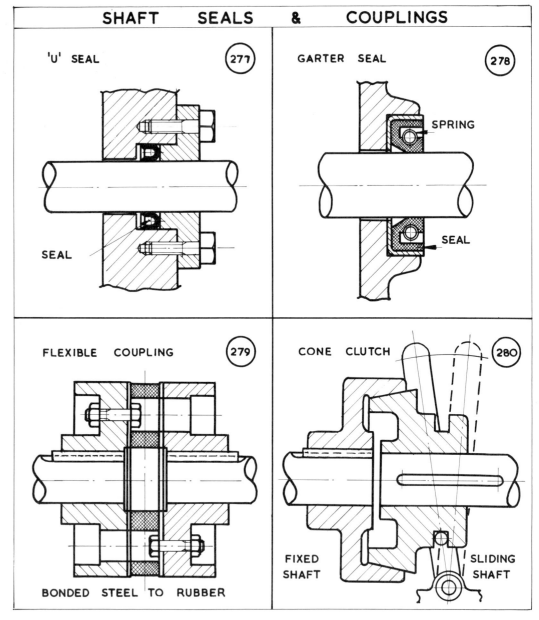

SHAFT   SEALS   &   COUPLINGS

'U' SEAL   277

SEAL

GARTER SEAL   278

SPRING

SEAL

FLEXIBLE   COUPLING   279

BONDED STEEL TO RUBBER

CONE CLUTCH   280

FIXED SHAFT

SLIDING SHAFT

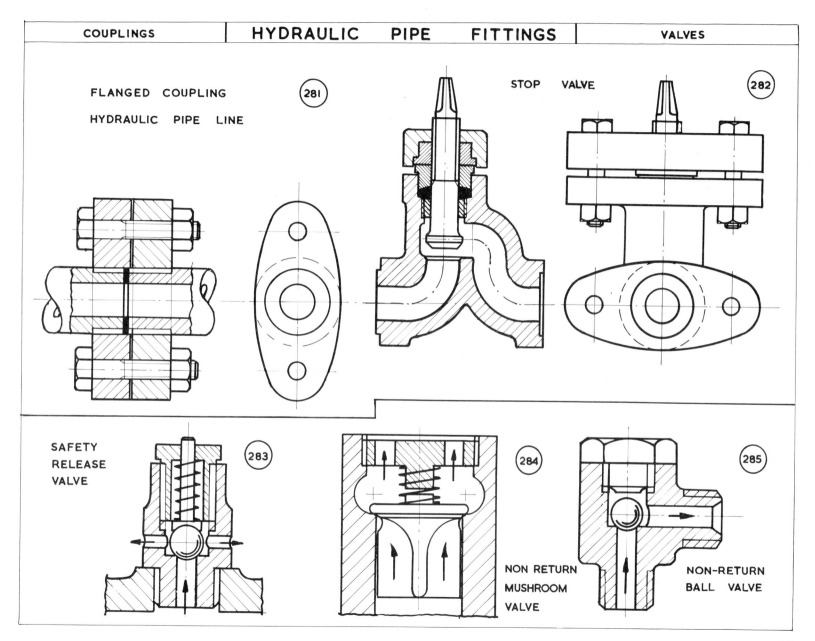

FLANGED COUPLING

HYDRAULIC PIPE LINE

281

STOP VALVE

282

SAFETY
RELEASE
VALVE

283

284

NON RETURN

MUSHROOM

VALVE

285

NON-RETURN
BALL VALVE

MACHINE DRAWING

The next pages deal progressively with the projection of orthographic views, in first angle and in third angle, beginning with simple exercises and reaching O Level standard examination questions later. About half the exercises are set in metric terms to give equal practice.

286. Angle Bracket A. An isometric view is given.
(a) Draw, in first angle, an elevation indicated by the arrow; project a plan. Project an end elevation to the right. A part solution is given.
(b) Draw, in third angle, the views mentioned above.

287. Vee Block B. An isometric view is given.
(a) Draw, in first angle, an elevation indicated by the arrow; project a plan. Project a sectional end elevation to the left of the front elevation, section taken on the centre line of the tee slots.
(b) Draw the above views using third angle.

288. Footstep Bearing An isometric view is given.
(a) Draw, in first angle, a sectional front elevation as indicated by the arrow; project a plan. Project an end elevation to the right of the elevation.
(b) Repeat the views using third angle.

289. Bearing Plate The isometric view is given.
(a) Draw, in first angle, the elevation in the direction of the arrow; project a plan and an end elevation to the left.
(b) Draw the views mentioned above, but using third angle projection.

290. End Plate The oblique view is given.
(a) Draw, in first angle, the elevation in the direction of the arrow; project a sectional plan taken on the centre line; project an end elevation to the right.
(b) Draw the views mentioned above in third angle.

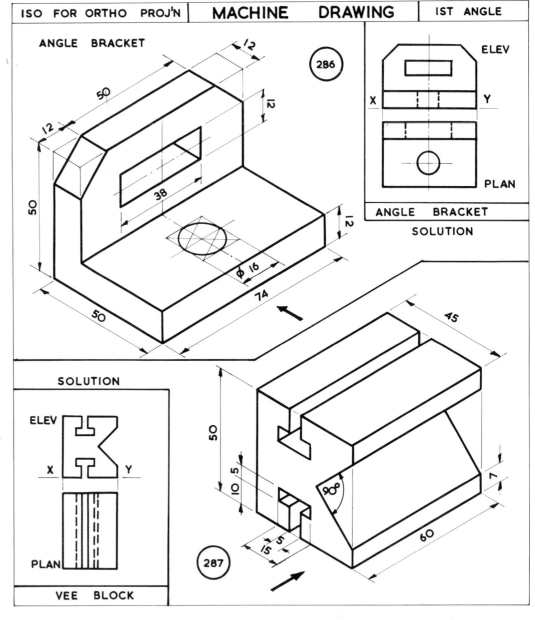

144

MACHINE DRAWING

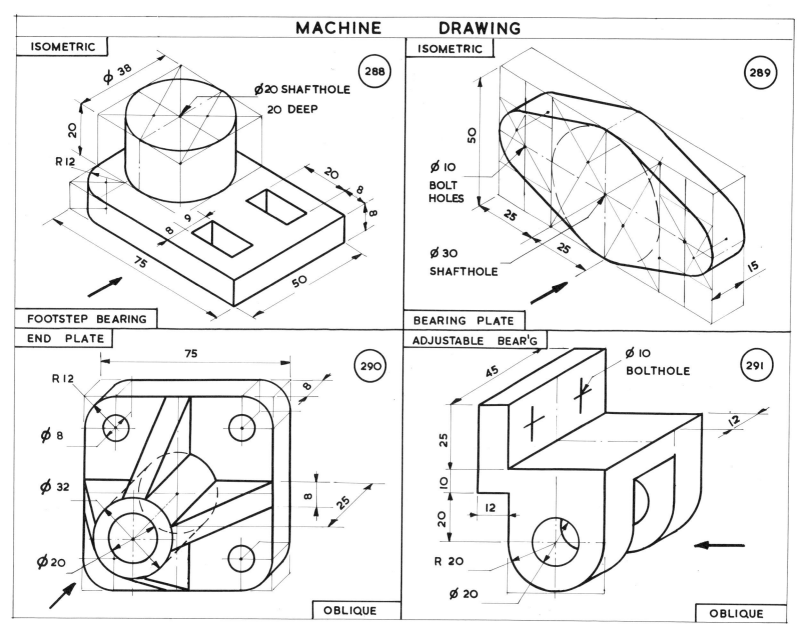

ISOMETRIC

288

ϕ 38

ϕ20 SHAFTHOLE
20 DEEP

20

R 12

20

8

8

9

8

75

50

FOOTSTEP BEARING

ISOMETRIC

289

50

ϕ 10
BOLT
HOLES

25

25

ϕ 30
SHAFTHOLE

15

BEARING PLATE

END PLATE

290

75

R 12

8

ϕ 8

ϕ 32

8

25

ϕ 20

OBLIQUE

ADJUSTABLE BEAR'G

291

ϕ 10
BOLTHOLE

45

12

25

10

12

20

R 20

ϕ 20

OBLIQUE

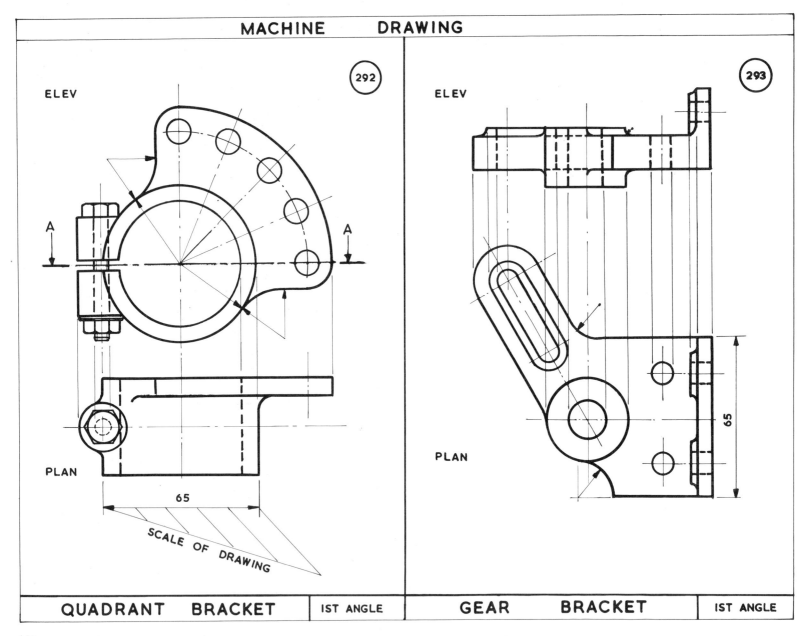

ELEV

292

A A

PLAN

65

SCALE OF DRAWING

ELEV

293

PLAN

65

| QUADRANT BRACKET | 1ST ANGLE |

| GEAR BRACKET | 1ST ANGLE |

291. Adjustable Bearing The oblique view is given.
(a) Draw, in first angle, the elevation as indicated by the arrow; project a plan, project also an end elevation to the right. Project an auxiliary elevation at 60° to the X Y line.
(b) Draw the above views using third angle.
  Further practice may be obtained with the object turned through an angle. Also take the existing plan and use it as an elevation and draw the projections from this. See 149.

292. Quadrant Bracket Two views of the bracket are given in first angle. Make a scale enabling sizes on the printed sheet to be repeated full size.
(a) Draw, using first angle, the elevation given and project a sectional plan as indicated by the section line A A. Draw a full end elevation to the right of the elevation.
(b) Repeat the above views using third angle projection.

293. Gear Bracket Two views in first angle are given on the bracket. Measurements may be obtained from the scale using dividers on the printed drawing.
(a) Draw, in first angle, the given plan and project the elevation, sectional on the centre line of the shaft hole. Project an end elevation to the right of the front elevation.
(b) Draw in third angle, the views mentioned above.

294. Ballrace Housing Two views in third angle are shown.
(a) Draw the given views, project a sectional end elevation to the left of the given elevation.
(b) Draw the given views as seen in first angle projection. Add an auxiliary elevation at an angle of 45° to the X Y line.
(c) In first angle projection, draw the given plan as shown as an elevation. Project a plan from this view; add a sectional end elevation to the right of the front elevation.

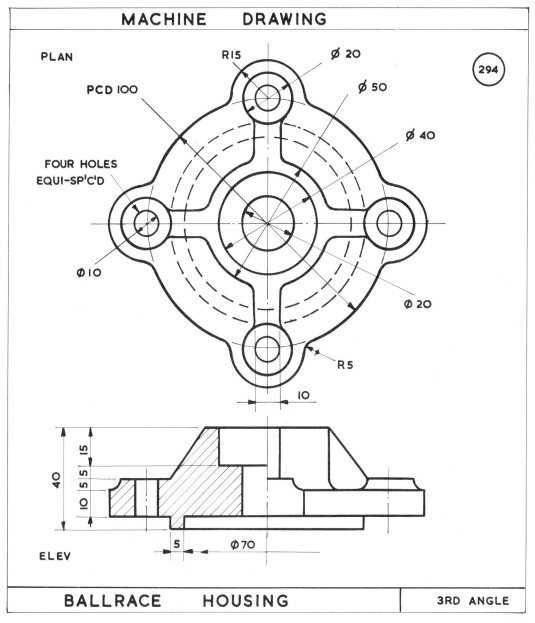

MACHINE DRAWING

294

PLAN

R15 Ø 20 Ø 50 PCD 100 Ø 40 FOUR HOLES EQUI-SP'C'D Ø 10 Ø 20 R 5 10

ELEV 15 5 5 10 40 5 Ø 70

BALLRACE HOUSING   3RD ANGLE

147

295. Quadrant Angle Bracket The bracket is shown in third angle projection.

(a) Draw the given views as shown. Project an end view sectional on the centre line of the shaft line.

(b) Project the views stated above in first angle.

296. Adjustable Clamp First angle views of the clamp are given.

(a) Draw the views as given, add an end elevation projected to the righthand.

(b) Draw, first angle, plan and elevation of each of the parts to be made in the workshop. See 317 for layout.

297. Quick Release Clamp Three views of the clamp are given in first angle projection.

(a) Draw the given views.

(b) Make first angle plans and elevations of the individual pieces of the clamp as diagrams suitable for the workshop. List all the parts. See 317 for layout.

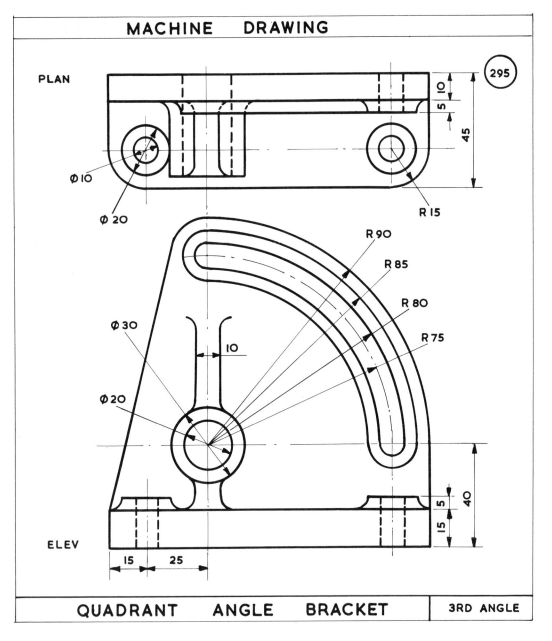

MACHINE DRAWING

PLAN

295

Ø10

Ø20

R15

R90

R85

R80

R75

Ø30

10

Ø20

15 25

ELEV

45

5 10

40

5 15

QUADRANT ANGLE BRACKET

3RD ANGLE

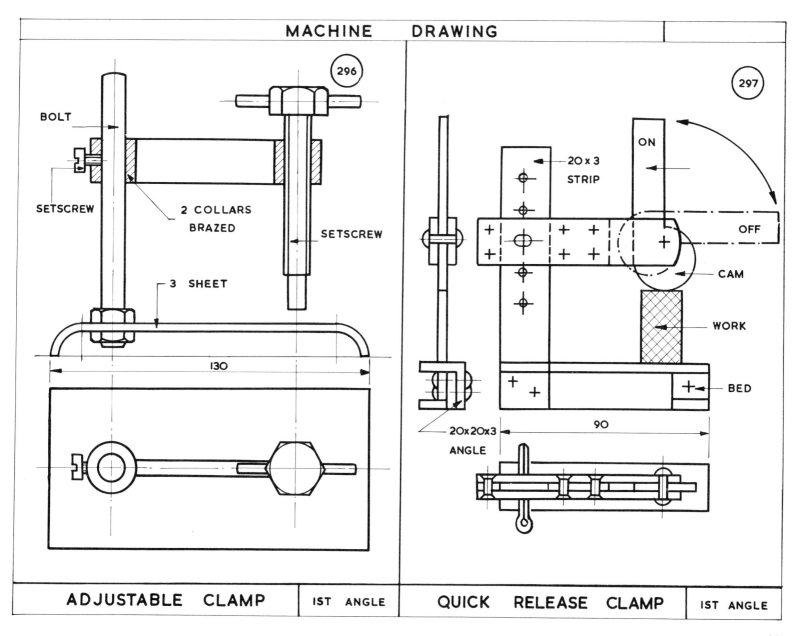

BOLT

SETSCREW

2 COLLARS
BRAZED

SETSCREW

3 SHEET

130

296

ADJUSTABLE CLAMP | IST ANGLE

20 x 3
STRIP

ON

OFF

CAM

WORK

BED

20x20x3
ANGLE

90

297

QUICK RELEASE CLAMP | IST ANGLE

149

298. Knuckle Joint First angle views are given of a knuckle joint used in a valve rod and link.

(*a*) Draw the views as shown.

(*b*) Draw the parts separately in first angle projection, plan and elevation, fully dimensioned. List the four parts as in 317.

299. Bearing Bracket First angle views of the bracket are given. A list of parts is shown also.

(*a*) Draw the views as shown; add the list.

(*b*) Draw the parts separately, three views of the the bracket, two views of other parts.

(*c*) Draw the given views using third angle projection.

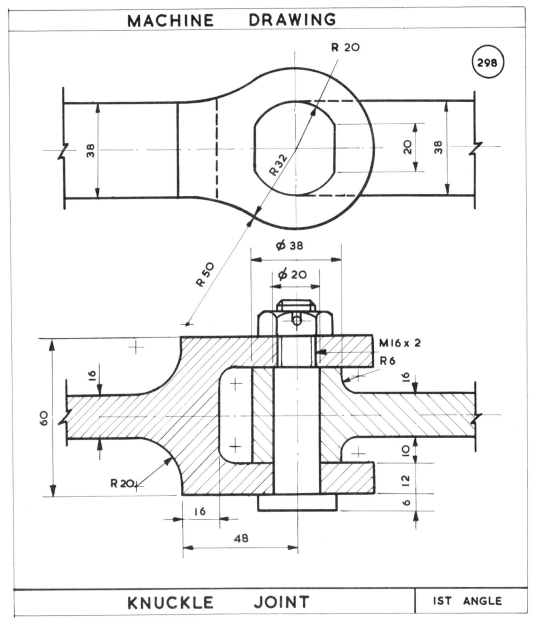

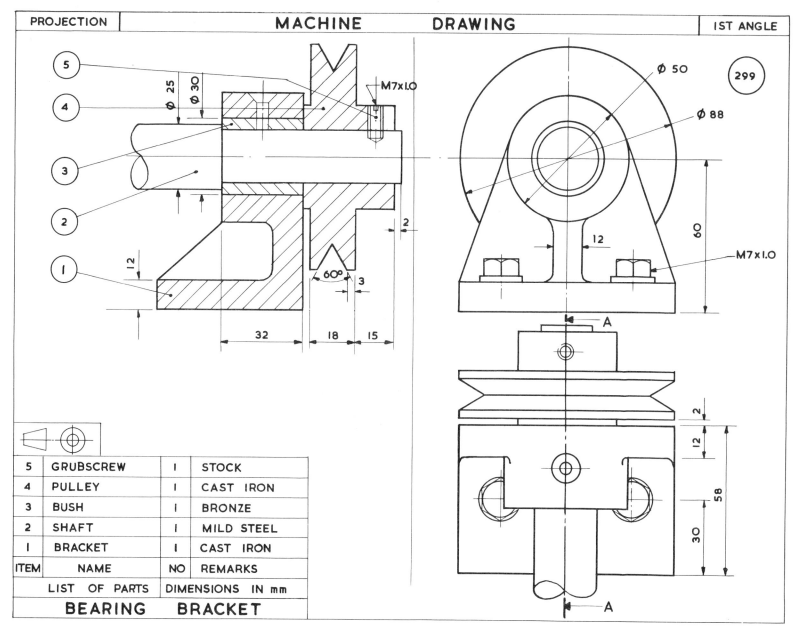

5	GRUBSCREW	I	STOCK
4	PULLEY	I	CAST IRON
3	BUSH	I	BRONZE
2	SHAFT	I	MILD STEEL
I	BRACKET	I	CAST IRON
ITEM	NAME	NO	REMARKS
	LIST OF PARTS		DIMENSIONS IN mm

BEARING BRACKET

151

300. Turned Shaft An elevation of the shaft is given. Draw in third angle, plan and elevation of each of the parts separately. List the details of the parts as in 317.

301. Turned Shaft An elevation of the shaft is given. Draw the view, and project both end views in third angle.

302. Gearbox Casing Two views of one half of the casing are shown with the sections of the two gears in position.

(*a*) Draw, in first angle, the gearbox assembled, the second half is a replica of the one shown, except that it is drilled and tapped for the bolts indicated, which are M7 × 1, 25 mm in length. The plan should be in full; the elevation sectional.

(*b*) Draw, in third angle, plan and elevation of the new side of the casing only. The drawing should be clear and fully dimensioned.

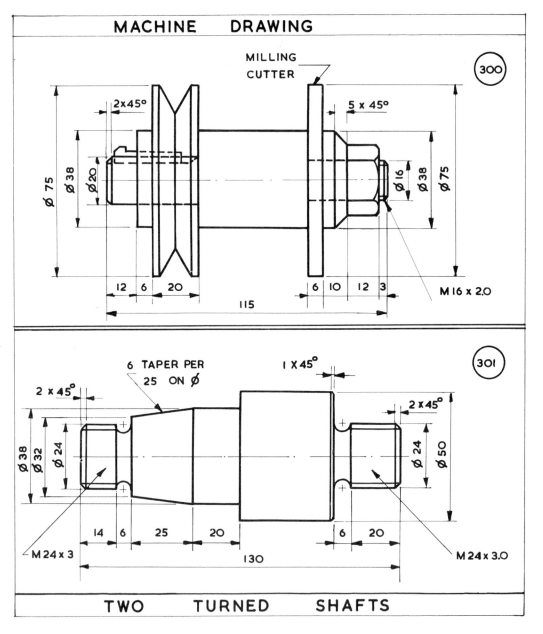

MACHINE DRAWING

TWO TURNED SHAFTS

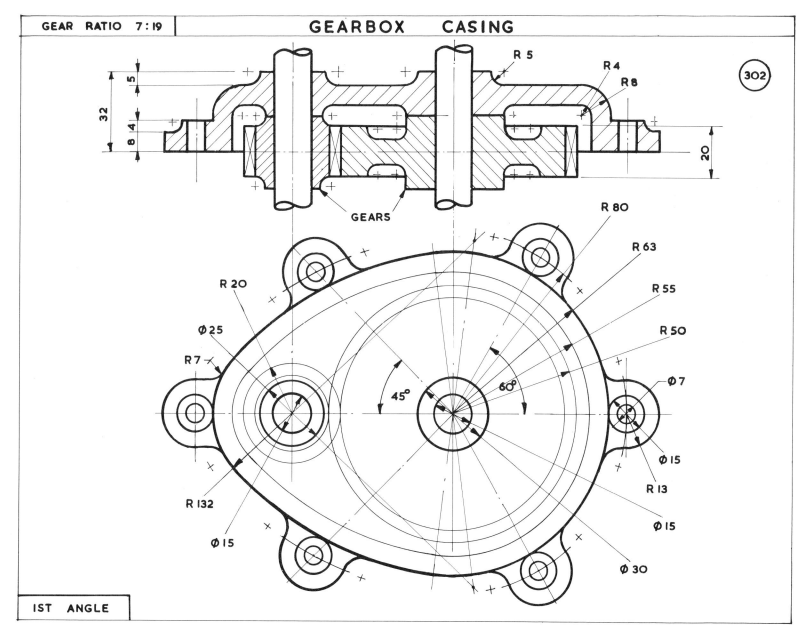

GEAR RATIO 7:19

GEARBOX CASING

R 5

R 4

R 8

302

5

32

8 14

20

GEARS

R 80

R 63

R 20

R 55

Ø 25

R 50

R 7

Ø 7

45°

60°

Ø 15

R 13

R 132

Ø 15

Ø 15

Ø 30

1ST ANGLE

153

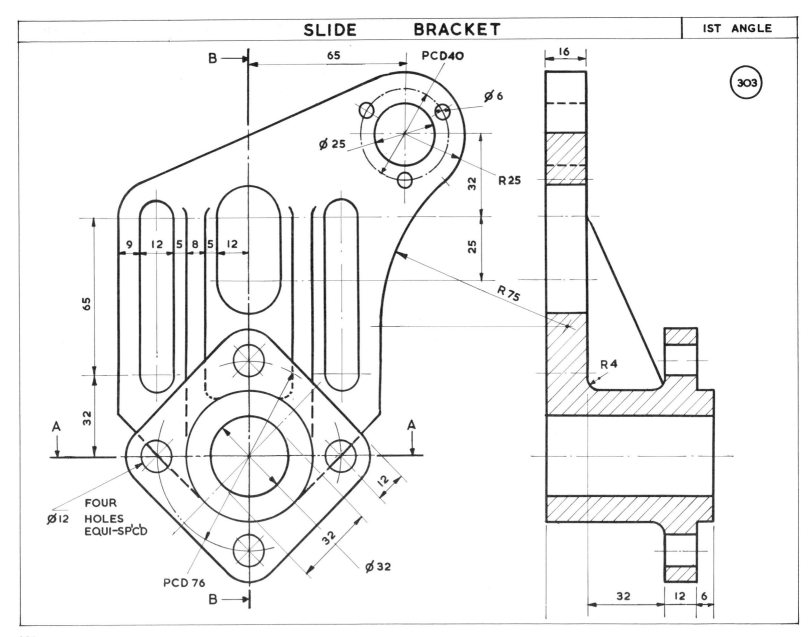

303

303. Slide Bracket Two views in first angle are given.

(*a*) Draw the given views, add a plan, section A A.

(*b*) Draw the views in third angle projection. Add a plan, sectioned as indicated at A A.

304. Gearbox Endplate Third angle views are given of the endplate.

(*a*) Draw the plan as shown; project an elevation sectioned as indicated.

(*b*) Project an end elevation to the left.

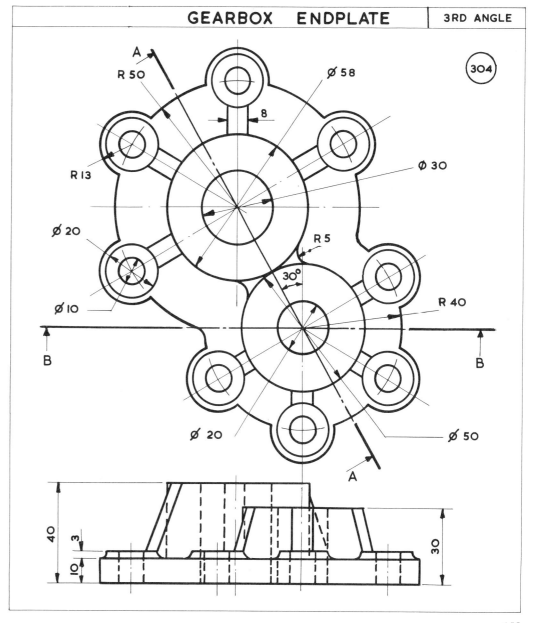

GEARBOX ENDPLATE 3RD ANGLE

304

A

R 50

Ø 58

8

R 13

Ø 30

Ø 20

R 5

Ø 10

30°

R 40

B

B

Ø 20

Ø 50

A

40

3

10

30

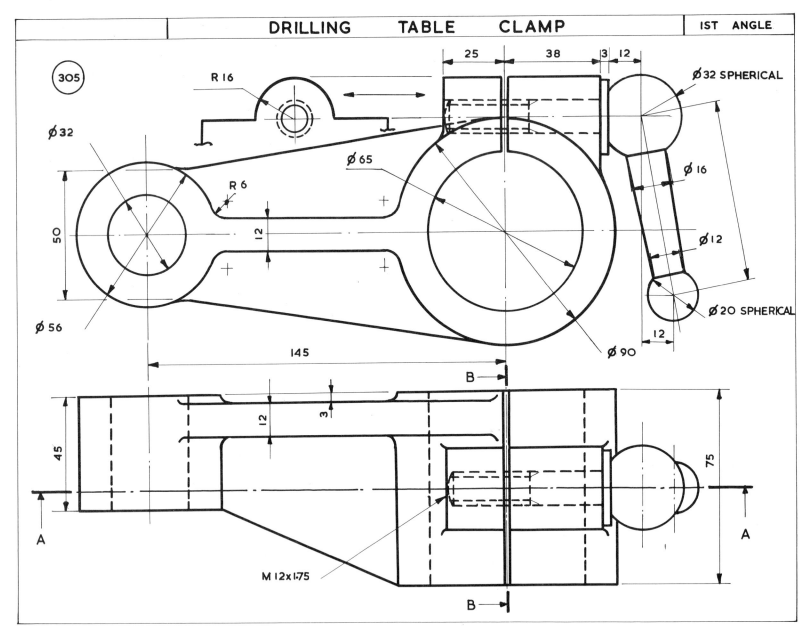

305

R 16

Ø 32

R 6

50

Ø 56

12

Ø 65

145

25

38

3

12

Ø 32 SPHERICAL

Ø 16

Ø 12

Ø 20 SPHERICAL

12

Ø 90

B

45

12

3

75

A

A

M 12 x 1.75

B

156

305. Drilling Table Clamp First angle views are given of the clamp.

(*a*) Draw in first angle, the given plan, and project a sectioned elevation as indicated by the line AA. Project an end elevation which shows the screw handle clearly. Dimension fully.

(*b*) Draw the views mentioned above, in third angle.

306. Gearbox Endplate The endplate is shown in first angle. Draw the views shown, project an end elevation to the left of the front elevation also sectioned on the centre line. Dimension fully.

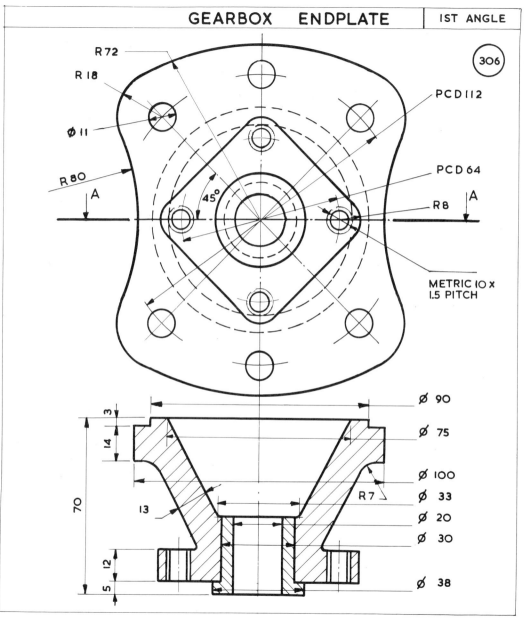

GEARBOX ENDPLATE | 1ST ANGLE

306

R 72

R 18

PCD 112

Ø 11

PCD 64

R 80

A

45°

A

R 8

METRIC 10 x 1.5 PITCH

Ø 90

3

14

Ø 75

70

Ø 100

R 7

Ø 33

13

Ø 20

Ø 30

12

5

Ø 38

157

307. Pump Endplate First angle views are shown, with the parts numbered.

(*a*) Draw the views as shown, project a plan, from the sectioned elevation.

(*b*) In first angle, draw the parts separately as numbered. Three views will be necessary of the endplate and also the gland; only two views of the bushes; elevation only of a bolt; two views of the seal.

(*c*) List the parts as in 317.

308. Universal Coupling This coupling enables two shafts to be coupled together, allowing movement of the shafts radially whilst the shafts are turning. The sliding splines also allow of extension during movement. The parts are shown drawn separately as in a workshop production drawing, first angle.

Draw the parts assembled in first angle projection; plan and elevation.

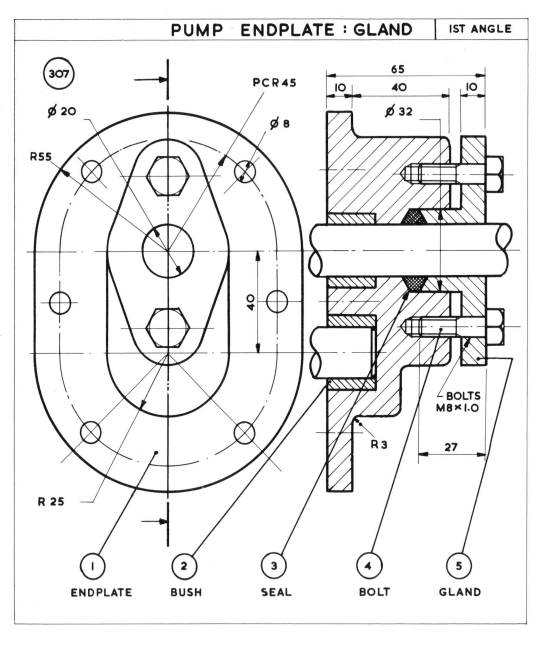

PUMP ENDPLATE : GLAND | 1ST ANGLE

ENDPLATE   BUSH   SEAL   BOLT   GLAND

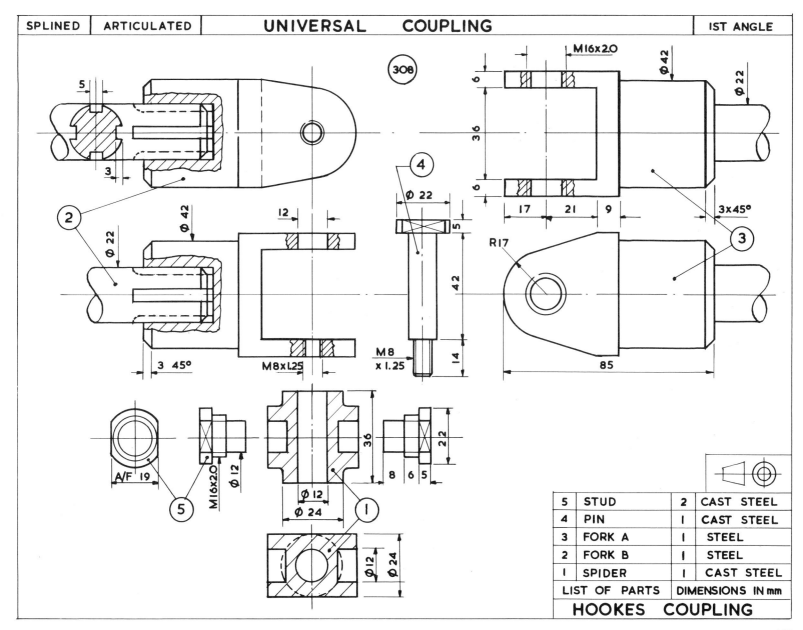

308

5	STUD	2	CAST STEEL
4	PIN	1	CAST STEEL
3	FORK A	1	STEEL
2	FORK B	1	STEEL
1	SPIDER	1	CAST STEEL
LIST OF PARTS		DIMENSIONS IN mm	

HOOKES   COUPLING

309. Cylinder Head First angle views are shown, the elevation being sectioned.

Draw, in first angle, the plan and elevation as shown; project an end elevation as indicated by the section line A A. Project a full end elevation to the opposite hand to the first end elevation.

310. Toggle-action Punch (*a*) Draw the two first angle views, as given, sizes and proportions of details are left to discretion. Sizes of base are suggested.

(*b*) Draw, in first angle, the parts separately, plan and elevation will be sufficient of each, except bolts. Tabulate the parts as in 317.

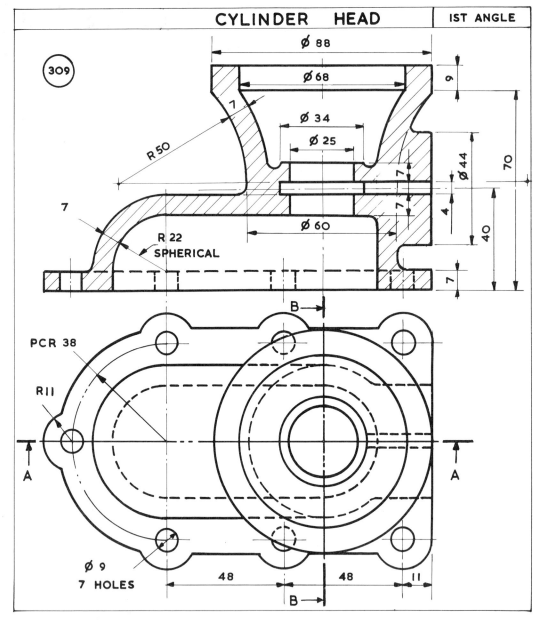

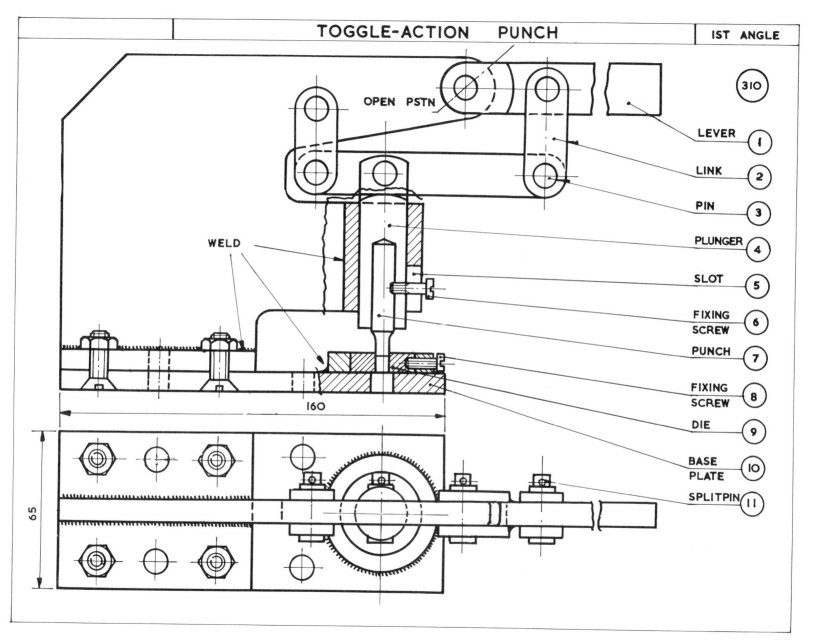

TOGGLE-ACTION PUNCH

OPEN PSTN

WELD

310

LEVER ①

LINK ②

PIN ③

PLUNGER ④

SLOT ⑤

FIXING SCREW ⑥

PUNCH ⑦

FIXING SCREW ⑧

DIE ⑨

BASE PLATE ⑩

SPLITPIN ⑪

160

65

311. Double-acting Lever Pump The pump is shown in two first angle views, the elevation sectioned.

(a) Draw the views as given, working proportionately from the diameter of the pump ram.

(b) In first angle, draw the parts separately as shown in the numbered list; plan and elevation of each as required to give full detail.

The pump body is made from stock brass hexagonal rod, strip, silver-soldered together. The ball valves are stainless steel, as are the rams, and top lever. The valve seats are turned from brass hexagonal rod. The gland nuts are from similar material. The seal rings are of greased hemp. The setscrews are of brass, as are the bolts.

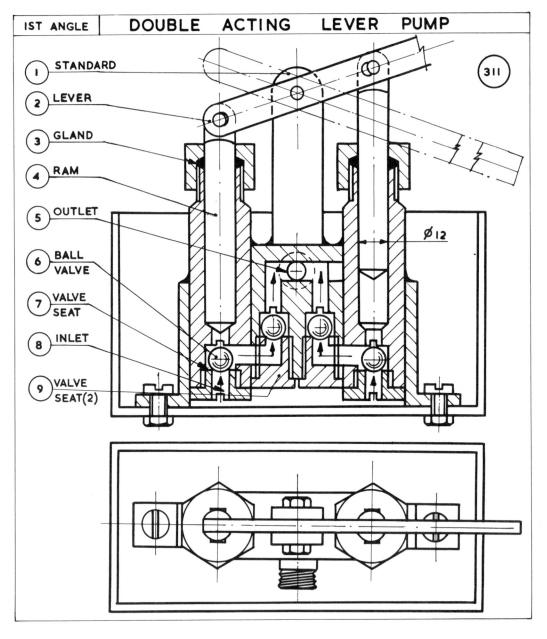

IST ANGLE

DOUBLE ACTING LEVER PUMP

311

1. STANDARD
2. LEVER
3. GLAND
4. RAM
5. OUTLET
6. BALL VALVE
7. VALVE SEAT
8. INLET
9. VALVE SEAT(2)

Ø12

312. Rotary Pump First angle views of the pump are given. The front cover has been removed in the elevation to show the rotor.

(a) Draw the given front elevation, project a plan in third angle sectioned as shown. Project an end elevation to the right of the elevation.

(b) Draw the parts of the pump separately in third angle, giving full details for production in the workshop. The list is given:

1. Pump Body   Brass casting
2. Rotor   Mild steel
3. Blades (6)   Bronze
4. Bush   Bronze
5. Back cover plate Brass
6. Sealing Ring   Hemp
7. Pulley; grubscrew Alloy
8. Front Cover   Brass
9. Springs (6)   Bronze
10. Setscrews (6)   Brass
11. C/S Setscrews (4) Brass

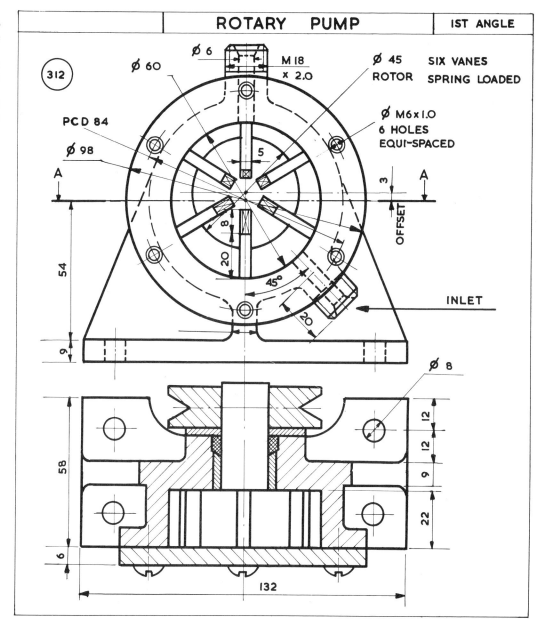

ROTARY PUMP — 1ST ANGLE

163

313. Cam Operated Shutter Unit First angle projections are shown of a light shutter operated by a cam shaft which lifts a shutter sliding in vee-grooves and spring loaded. The shutter is shown in the open position. The parts are listed.

Draw the given views in third angle. List the parts as shown in 317.

314. Parts of the Cam Operated Shutter The parts are shown in full detail, in first angle.

In third angle, draw the working drawings of the parts shown in the diagrams. Adopt the same numbering.

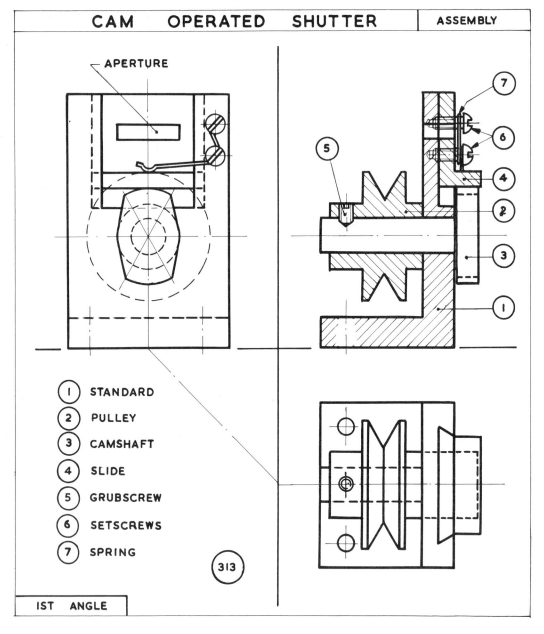

CAM OPERATED SHUTTER | ASSEMBLY

APERTURE

1 STANDARD
2 PULLEY
3 CAMSHAFT
4 SLIDE
5 GRUBSCREW
6 SETSCREWS
7 SPRING

313

1ST ANGLE

PARTS FOR CAM OPERATED SHUTTER

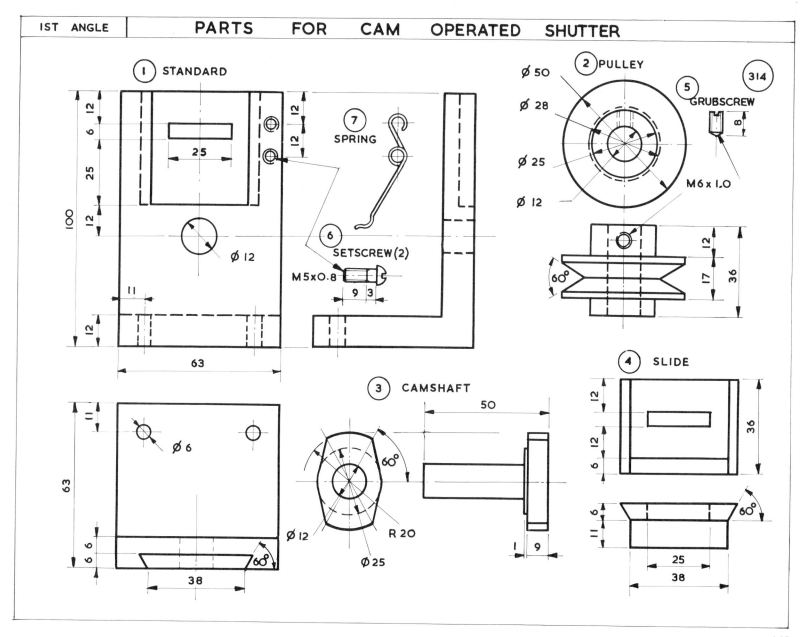

① STANDARD

② PULLEY

⑦ SPRING

⑥ SETSCREW(2)
M5x0.8

③ CAMSHAFT

④ SLIDE

⑤ GRUBSCREW
M6x1.0

⑬⑭

315. Ratchet and Pawl Assembly drawings, in third angle, are given. A list of the parts is also given.

(a) In first angle, draw the views given, taking the' left diagram as the front elevation. Project a plan. List the parts as in 317.

316. Parts for the Ratchet and Pawl The parts for the assembly are shown in detail in third angle.

(b) Draw in first angle, working drawing of the parts. Adopt the same numbering.

317. Oscillating Pump The assembly views in first angle projection are shown of the pump. A flywheel is used as a pulley to drive a crankshaft which raises and lowers the ram of the pump. The cylinder, which oscillates on a trunnion, is held to the valve-face by a spring and nut, and the single port in the cylinder uncovers the drilled inlet port in the standard on the suction charging stroke, to give delivery through the outlet port.

A list of parts is given in detail at the foot of the page.

(a) In third angle, draw the views. Project a plan.

318. Parts for the Oscillating Pump Detail drawings of the parts are shown in first angle.

(b) In third angle, draw detail drawings of the parts shown. Adopt the same numbering.

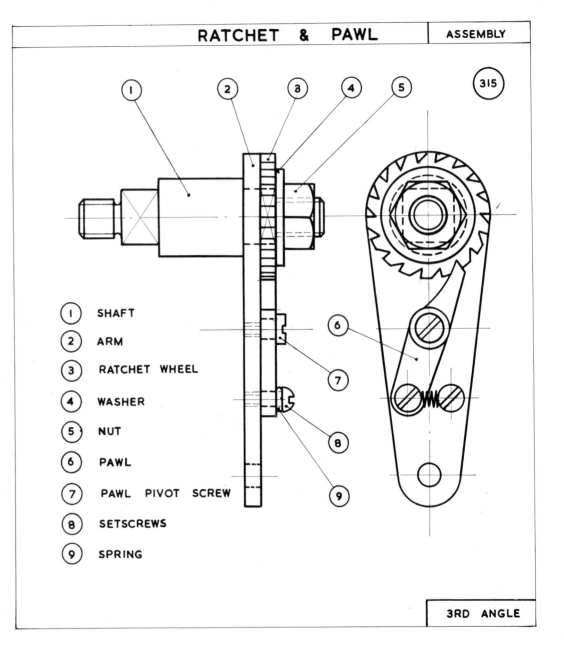

RATCHET & PAWL   ASSEMBLY

315

1 SHAFT
2 ARM
3 RATCHET WHEEL
4 WASHER
5 NUT
6 PAWL
7 PAWL PIVOT SCREW
8 SETSCREWS
9 SPRING

3RD ANGLE

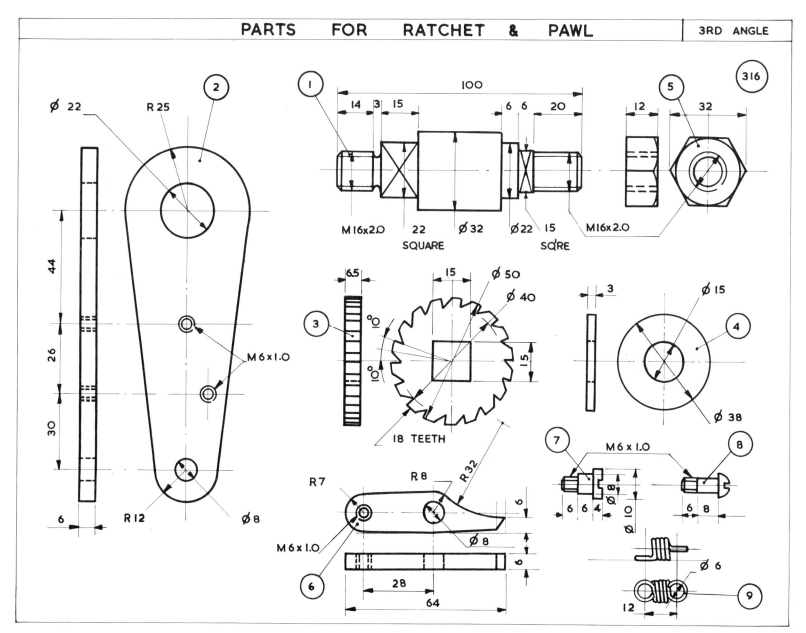

316

① 100

14 3 15 6 6 20

M16x2.0 22 Ø 32 Ø 22 15 M16x2.0
SQUARE SQRE

② Ø 22 R 25

44 26 30 6

M6x1.0

R12 Ø 8

⑤ 12 32

③ 6.5 15 Ø 50 Ø 40
10° 10° 15
18 TEETH

④ 3 Ø 15 Ø 38

⑥ R7 R8 R32
M6x1.0 Ø 8 6 6
28 64

⑦ M6x1.0 ⑧
6 6 4 Ø 8 Ø 10 6 8

⑨ Ø 6
12

167

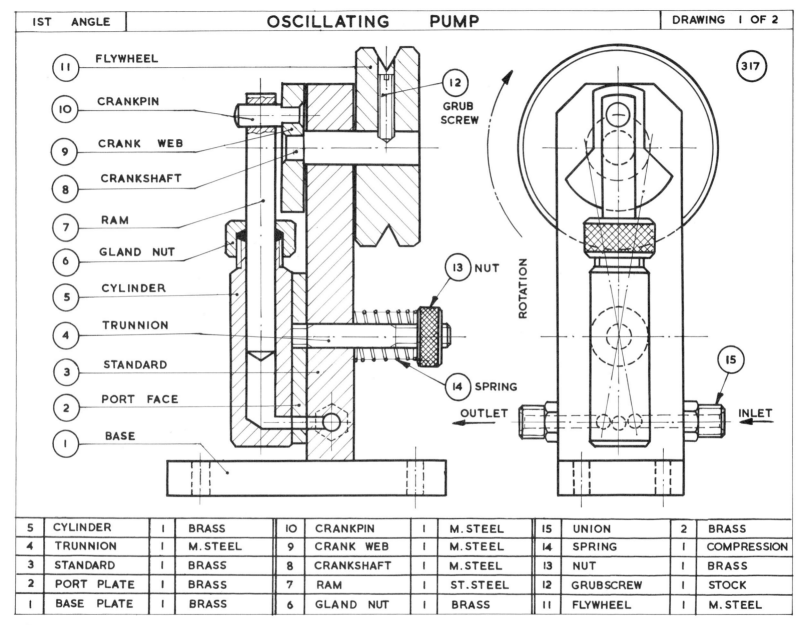

5	CYLINDER	1	BRASS	10	CRANKPIN	1	M. STEEL	15	UNION	2	BRASS
4	TRUNNION	1	M. STEEL	9	CRANK WEB	1	M. STEEL	14	SPRING	1	COMPRESSION
3	STANDARD	1	BRASS	8	CRANKSHAFT	1	M. STEEL	13	NUT	1	BRASS
2	PORT PLATE	1	BRASS	7	RAM	1	ST. STEEL	12	GRUBSCREW	1	STOCK
1	BASE PLATE	1	BRASS	6	GLAND NUT	1	BRASS	11	FLYWHEEL	1	M. STEEL

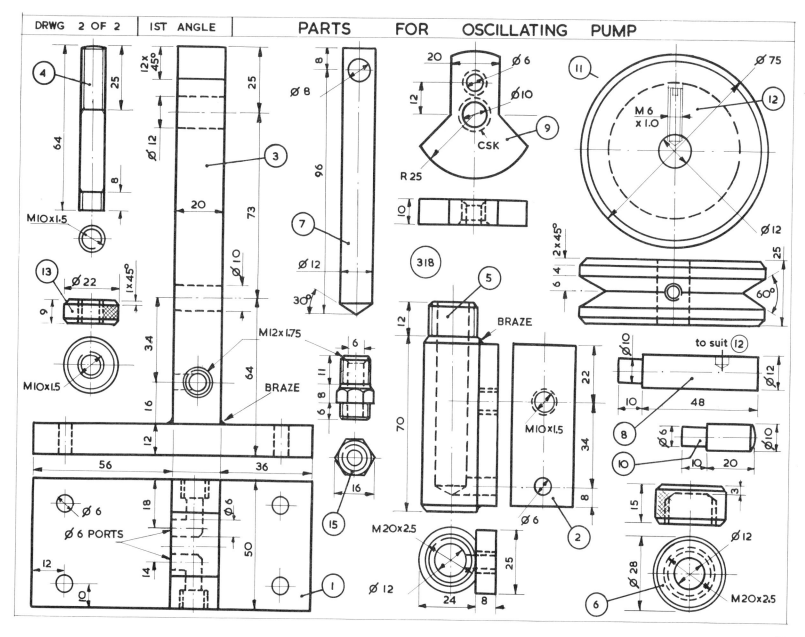

4

25
12 x 45°
25
Ø 12
64
8

M10x1.5

13
Ø 22
1 x 45°
9
M10x1.5

3
20
73
10
Ø10
34
M12x1.75
64
16
BRAZE
12
56
36

18
Ø 6
Ø 6
Ø 6 PORTS
12
14
50
10
1

Ø 8
8
96
7
Ø 12
30°

318

6
8
11
6
BRAZE
16
15

20
Ø 6
12
Ø10
CSK
R 25
9
10

5
12
70
34
22
8
Ø 6
M10x1.5
BRAZE
2
M20x2.5
Ø 12
24
8
25

11
Ø 75
12
M 6 x 1.0
Ø 12

2 x 45°
6 4
25
60°

Ø10
to suit 12
Ø12
10
48
8

Ø 6
Ø10
10
10
20

15
3
Ø 12
Ø 28
M20x2.5
6

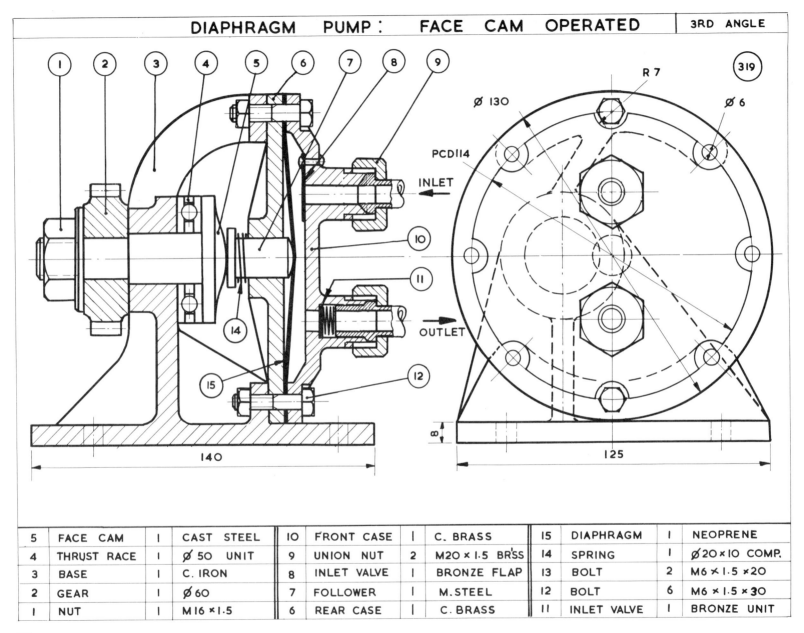

DIAPHRAGM PUMP: FACE CAM OPERATED

3RD ANGLE

5	FACE CAM	1	CAST STEEL	10	FRONT CASE	1	C. BRASS	15	DIAPHRAGM	1	NEOPRENE
4	THRUST RACE	1	Ø 50 UNIT	9	UNION NUT	2	M20 × 1.5 BR'SS	14	SPRING	1	Ø20 × 10 COMP.
3	BASE	1	C. IRON	8	INLET VALVE	1	BRONZE FLAP	13	BOLT	2	M6 × 1.5 × 20
2	GEAR	1	Ø 60	7	FOLLOWER	1	M. STEEL	12	BOLT	6	M6 × 1.5 × 30
1	NUT	1	M16 × 1.5	6	REAR CASE	1	C. BRASS	11	INLET VALVE	1	BRONZE UNIT

170

319. Diaphragm Pump Assembly diagrams are shown of a pump whose neoprene plastic diaphragm is actuated by a face cam, gear driven. Flap valves are used to give a one-way flow as indicated by the flow-arrows. As the face cam presses the follower, the diaphragm gives the pressure pulse, in delivery. The suction is made when the diaphragm returns by its own elasticity after the cam lift. Third angle projection is used; a list of parts is also given.

(a) In first angle, draw the two views in the correct projection. Project a plan under the sectioned view. List the parts.

(b) In first angle, draw detail drawings of the separate parts as shown in the list. Adopt the same numbering.

320. A Contact Breaker Unit A gear-driven eccentric actuates a link-pivoted strap which pecks at a spring-loaded contact trigger once every revolution. The unit is arranged on a back plate.

Two full views are given in third angle projection.

(a) Draw, as shown, the plan and elevation; project both end elevations.

(b) Draw detail drawings of the parts separately also in third angle.

Make a list of parts, tabulated. Parts:

1. Backplate
2. Eccentric shaft
3. Nut
4. Eccentric Strap
5. Link Pivot Screw
6. Trigger
7. Bracket
8. Spring
9. Trigger Pivot
10. Stop Pin
11. Strap Bolts (2)
12. Bracket Screws (2)

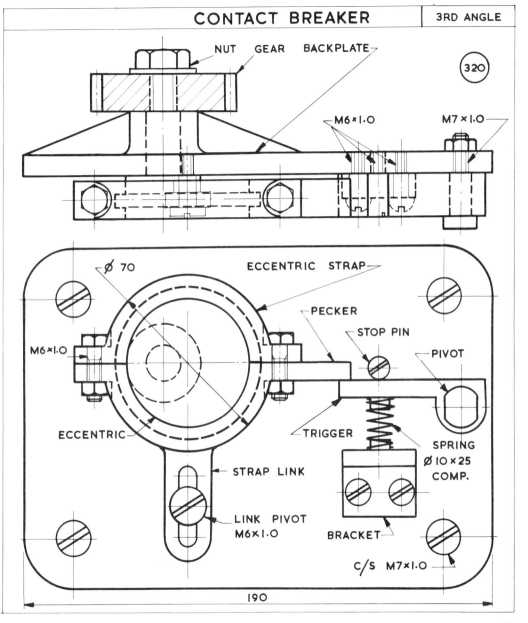

CONTACT BREAKER — 3RD ANGLE

321. Disc Valve Pump First angle views of the pump are given. The valve rod works a hollow plunger which has a spring loaded disc valve on its upper surface. The lower valve works on a centre pin. An annulus is turned in the cylinder wall, and a sealing ring fits therein.

On the upward charging stroke, the lower valve lifts to allow the cylinder to fill, the top valve remaining closed under back pressure. The downward stroke closes the bottom valve, and the pressure opens the top valve allowing fluid to be delivered at the outlet.

A list of parts is given.

In third angle, draw the two given views correctly placed. Project a full end elevation showing the inlet and outlet orifices.

322. Parts for the Disc Valve Pump The parts of the pump are shown in third angle projection, in detail.

In first angle, draw the parts as shown separately in detail.

323. Lathe Slide The top slide of a lathe is shown, two sizes being given.
(a) Draw the two views as shown in first angle, scaling up the sizes from the printed diagram. Use discretion on the details where no sizes are given. Project a plan under the righthand diagram.
(b) In first angle, draw the separate parts in detail.

324. Square Toolbox Draw the parts separately in detail, using the scale to obtain sizes.

325. Lifting Toolbox used on a shaping machine. Draw the parts separately in detail, using the scale to obtain sizes.

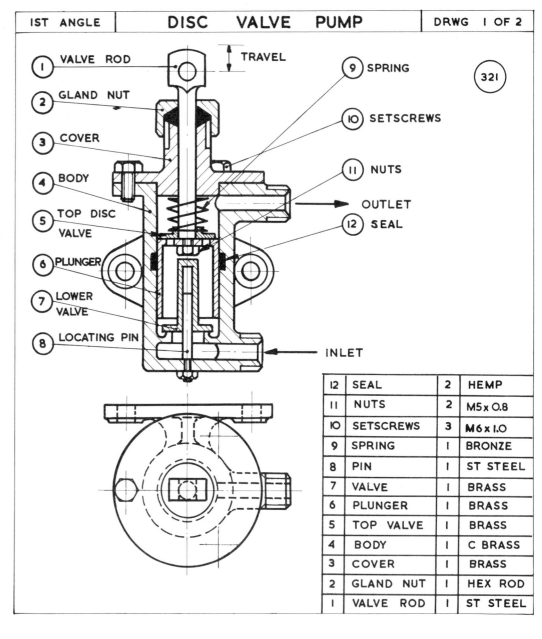

12	SEAL	2	HEMP
11	NUTS	2	M5 x 0.8
10	SETSCREWS	3	M6 x 1.0
9	SPRING	1	BRONZE
8	PIN	1	ST STEEL
7	VALVE	1	BRASS
6	PLUNGER	1	BRASS
5	TOP VALVE	1	BRASS
4	BODY	1	C BRASS
3	COVER	1	BRASS
2	GLAND NUT	1	HEX ROD
1	VALVE ROD	1	ST STEEL

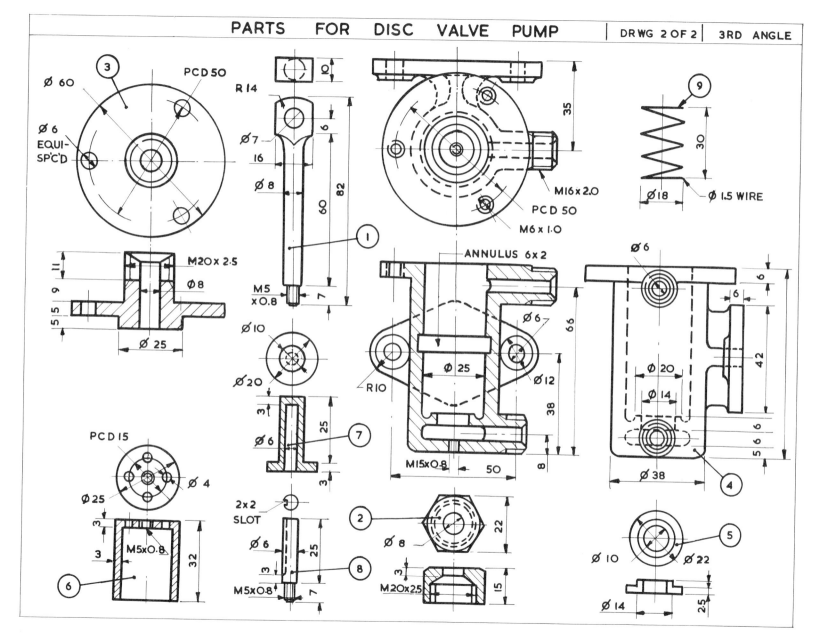

Ø 60
PCD 50
③
R 14

Ø 6
EQUI-
SP'C'D

Ø 7
16
Ø 8

82
60

6

10

35

⑨

30

Ø 18   Ø 1.5 WIRE

M16 x 2.0
PCD 50
M6 x 1.0

①

M5
x 0.8
7

M20 x 2.5
11
9
5 5
Ø 8
Ø 25

Ø 10
Ø 20
3
Ø 6
25
3
⑦

ANNULUS 6 x 2

Ø 6
Ø 25
R 10
Ø 12

66
38

8

M15 x 0.8   50

Ø 6
6
6
Ø 20
Ø 14
42
5 6
Ø 38
④

PCD 15

Ø 25
Ø 4

3
M5 x 0.8
3
32
⑥

2 x 2
SLOT

Ø 6
25
3
M5 x 0.8
7
⑧

②
Ø 8
22

3
M20 x 2.5
15

Ø 10   Ø 22
⑤
Ø 14
2.5

LATHE   SLIDE

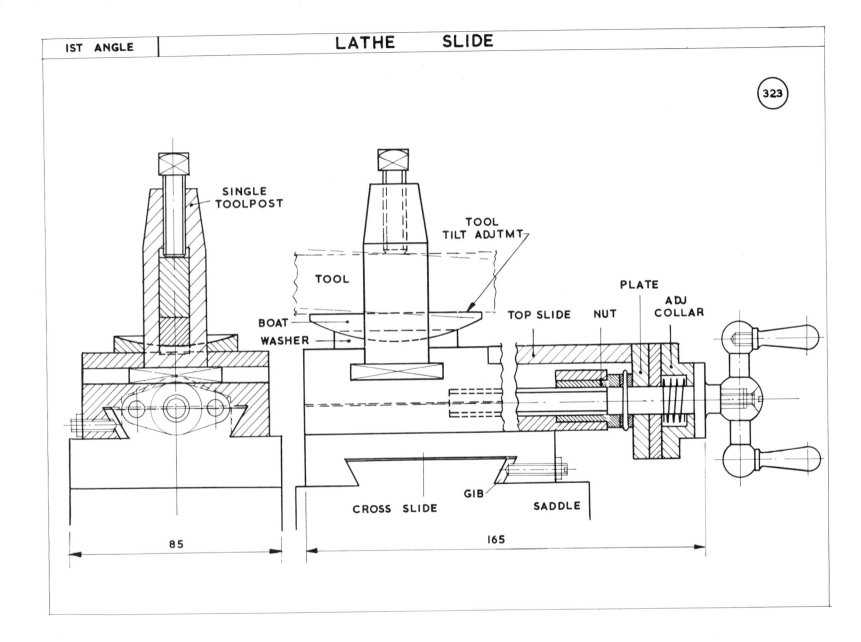

SINGLE
TOOLPOST

TOOL
TILT ADJTMT

TOOL

PLATE

ADJ
COLLAR

TOP SLIDE   NUT

BOAT
WASHER

GIB

CROSS   SLIDE

SADDLE

85

165

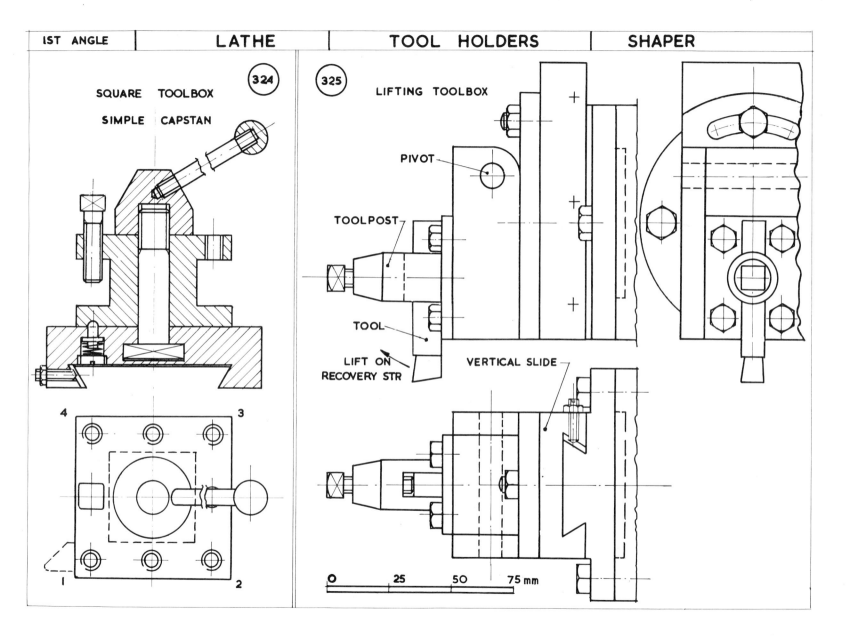

SQUARE TOOLBOX

SIMPLE CAPSTAN

324

325   LIFTING TOOLBOX

PIVOT

TOOLPOST

TOOL

LIFT ON
RECOVERY STR

VERTICAL SLIDE

4   3

1   2

O   25   50   75 mm

175

APPENDIX I

ISO Metric Screwthreads (sizes in mm)	
Diam.	Pitch
1·6	0·35
2	0·4
2·5	0·45
3	0·5
4	0·7
5	0·8
6	1·0
8	1·25
10	1·5
12	1·75
16	2·0
20	2·5
24	3·0
30	3·5
36	4·0

BS 3643: 1963 Part 1

Designation of Metric Screw threads

Material
Head shape
Bolt (or nut)
Diameter
Pitch
Length
Type of fit

Example

Steel
Hexagonal head
Bolt
$M10 \times 1·5 \times 30 - 8g$

Nut (or internal thread)
$M10 \times 1·5 - 7H$

BS 3643: 1963 Part 1

ISO Metric Screwed Studs $\emptyset = D$

$\emptyset$	Nominal Length	Metal End Length = D to $1\frac{1}{2}$D
M3		
M4	12	
M5	14	Plain Part Length = not less than $\frac{1}{2}$D
M6	16	
M8	20	
M10	25	
M12	30	Nut End Length = 2D + 6 mm
M16		

BS 4439: 1969 Table 1, Appdx D

Bolts and Nuts Class of Fits—general use		
	Bolt	Nut
Close	4h	5H
Medium	6g	6H
Free	8g	7H

BS 3643: 1966 Part 2

Selected Hole and Shaft Fits	Clearance		Transition		Interference	
	Hole	Shaft	Hole	Shaft	Hole	Shaft
Average	H8	f7	H7	n6	H7	s6
Fine	H7	g6	H7	k6	H7	n6
Examples	Clearance Fit H8–f7		Transition Fit H7-k6		Interference Fit H7-s6	

BS 4500: 1969 Part 1 Tables 6, 8

176

ISO Metric Machine Screws (steel)

$\emptyset$	Length	Slotted	Recessed
M3 M4 M5 M6 M8 M10	6 8 10 12 16 20 25	CSK RSD CSK PAN CHEESE	CSK RSD CSK PAN

BS 4183: 1967

ISO Metric Hexagon Socket Screws

$\emptyset$	Pitch	Length	Hexagon Socket A/F			
			CAP	CSK	SET	Button
M3	0·5	8	2·5	2·0	1·5	2·0
M4	0·7	10	3·0	2·5	2·0	2·5
M5	0·8	12	4·0	3·0	2·5	3·0
M6	1·0	16	5·0	4·0	3·0	4·0
M8	1·25	20	6·0	5·0	4·0	5·0
M10	1·5	25	8·0	6·0	5·0	6·0
M12	1·75	30	10·0	8·0	6·0	8·0

BS 4168: 1967 Tables 3, 4, 5, 6

Rivet $\emptyset = 6\sqrt{\text{(Plate Thickness)}}$

$\emptyset$ Rivet	Plate Thickness
2	0·11
2·5	0·2
3	0·3
4	0·5
5	0·7
6	1·0
8	2·0
10	3·0
12	4
16	8
20	12
24	16

BS 4620: 1970

Selection of Abbreviations

A/F	aross flats	$\emptyset$	diameter	SCR	screwed
ASSY	assembly	R	radius	SPHERE $\emptyset$	spherical diam
CRS	centres	DRG	drawing	SPHERE R	spherical radius
CL	centre line	HEX	hexagon	S'FACE	spot face
CHAM	chamfer	HEX HD	hexagon head	SQ or $\square$	square
CH HD	cheese head	INT	internal	STD	standard
CSK	countersunk	LH	left hand	U'CUT	undercut
CSK HD	countersunk head	NO	number	$\longrightarrow$	taper
C'BORE	counter bore	PCD	pitch circle diam		
CYL	cylinder	RD HD	round head		

BS 308:1

177

Ferrous Metals

Cast iron	Rigid castings
Malleable	
cast iron	Flexible
Steel, mild	General work
Steel, cast	Tools, cutters
Steel, nickel-chrome	Heavy duty
Steel, stainless	Chemical resistant
Steel, vanadium	Tough spanners
Steel, tungsten	Machine cutters

Non-ferrous Metals

Copper		Wire, sheet
Brass	Cu/Sn	General
Bronze	Cu/Sn/P	Bearings
Gun metal	Cu/Sn	
Nickel alloys		Acid resistant
Aluminium alloys	Al/Mg	Aircraft
Magnesium alloys	Al/Cu	Aircraft
Babbitt metal	Mg/Al	
Die cast metal	Sb/Cu/Zn	

SUGGESTIONS FOR SKETCHING DIAGRAMS

Tools Forging	Lathe
Anvil	Toolbit holder
Tongs	Boring tool
Hardies	Reamer
Cutters	End mill
Flatters	Spot facer
Hammers	Keyway cutter
Sledges	Tailstock dieholder
	Saddle topslide
Fitters	Milling slide
Files	
Vice	**Processes**
Surface plate	Plain turning
Vee block	Facing in chuck
Trysquare	Taper turning
Sliding callipers	Recess turning
Scriber	
Pliers	**Casting**
Tap wrench	Wood patterns
Dies and stock	Cored pattern
Drills	Simple casting
Shears	Cope and drag box casting

Selection of British Standards

46	Keys and keyways
292	Ball and roller bearings
308	1,2,3, Engineering drawing
3643	ISO Metric screwthreads
3763	International SI units
4183	Machine nuts and screws
4439	Screwed studs
4500	ISO Limits and fits
4620	Rivets

BSI Sales Branch
101 Pentonville Rd
London N1 9ND

Angular Measure

Degrees	Radians	Radians	Degrees
1	0·0175	0·01	0·57
2	0·0349	0·02	1·15
3	0·0524	0·03	1·72
4	0·0698	0·04	2·29
5	0·0873	0·05	2·86
10	0·1745	0·10	5·73
20	0·3491	0·20	11·46
30	0·5236	0·50	28·65
60	1·047	0·75	42·97
90	1·571	1·00	57·30
120	2·094	1·50	85·94
150	2·618	$\pi/2$	90·00
180	3·142	π	180·00
360	2π	2π	360·00

$$1 \text{ Radian} = \frac{180°}{\pi} = 57·2958°$$

$$1° = 0·0174533 \text{ radians}$$

Angular Velocity

1 radian per second	= 1 rad s^{-1}
	= 57·2958° per second
	= 9·5493 rev per min
360°	= 6·28318 rad
1°	= 0·0175 rad
1° per second	= 0·16667 rev per min
1 rev per min	= 6° per second
	= 0·10472 rad s^{-1}

BS 3763 Appdx A

Basic SI Units		
Quantity	**Name of Unit**	**Unit Symbol**
length	metre	m
mass	kilogram	kg
time	second	s
electric current	ampere	A
temperature	kelvin	K
force	newton	N
work	joule	J
power	watt	W
area	square metre	m^2
volume	cubic metre	m^3
frequency	hertz	Hz
density	kg per cubic metre	$kg\ m^{-3}$
velocity	metre per second	$m\ s^{-1}$
angular velocity	radian per second	$rad\ s^{-1}$
acceleration	metre per second squared	$m\ s^{-2}$
pressure	newton per square metre	$N\ m^{-2}$
momentum	mass × velocity	$kg\ m\ s^{-1}$
moment of force	newton	N m
weight of 1 kg mass		9·81 N
gravitational acceleration		$9·81\ m\ s^{-2}$
unit force × unit distance	=	work done
1 newton × 1 metre	=	1 joule
unit voltage × unit current	=	unit power
1 volt × 1 ampere	=	1 watt

BS 3763 Tables 1, 2, 4, 5

Multiples and Sub-multiples of SI Units		
Prefix	**Symbol**	**Factor**
exa	E	10^{18}
peta	P	10^{15}
tera	T	10^{12}
giga	G	10^{9}
mega	M	10^{6}
kilo	k	10^{3}
hecto	h	10^{2}
deca	da	10
UNIT	as list	1
deci	d	10^{-1}
centi	c	10^{-2}
milli	m	10^{-3}
micro	u	10^{-6}
nano	n	10^{-9}
pico	p	10^{-12}
femto	f	10^{-15}
atto	a	10^{-18}

BS 3763 Table 6

Examples			
A	$1\,005\,602\ m^2$	$=1·006 \times 10^6\ m^2$	$=1\ Mm^2$
B	$1\,000\ Gm^3$	$=1·0 \times 10^{12}\ m^3$	$=1\ Tm^3$
C	$5\ hm$	$=500\ m$	
D	$5\ kN$	$=5000\ N$	$=5 \times 10^3\ N$

For solutions to questions 1–32 see pp. 182–189

1. A triangle has two sides in the ratio of 5:6 and at an angle of 95°. Draw the triangle when the altitude is 55 mm. (Draw angle and sides as ratio, join ends and perpendicular, extend to 55 mm.)

2. Draw the triangle which has a base of 60 mm and an opposite angle of 65°. (Draw base and angle of 65°. Draw perpendicular to line and angle. Draw enclosing circle.)

3. Draw a regular hexagon of 35 mm side and construct a triangle of equal area. Find the incentre of the triangle. (After reduction, bisect angles to give incentre.)

4. Draw a hexagon of 40 mm side. Construct a triangle of equal area, and find its centre of gravity. (Draw hexagon by compass or setsquare. Intersection of medians gives C. of G.)

5. Draw a square equal in area to the two rectangles 1 and 2. (Reduce the triangles to one, then construct to square by mean proportional method.)

6. Draw a triangle, equal in area to the given triangle, but on a 125 mm base. (Draw rectangle equal to triangle, change to rectangle on new base, diagonal method; any triangle touching new altitude parallel.)

7. In the given triangle, draw a touching semicircle. Show construction. (Draw the triangle, bisect the angle shown, perpendiculars from the sides give radius of semicircle.)

8. In an angle of 30°, draw a circle which touches both arms of the angle and passes through a point P. (Draw the angle and point P. Bisect angle, and draw constructional circle first. Line through angle and point gives similar point to all circles.)

9. Find the pitch circles of three gears whose centres are given by the triangle, sides being 75 mm, 65 mm, 37 mm. (Draw the triangle, bisect the angles to give incentre; perpendiculars from sides give radii.)

10. A circle, line and point are given. Draw a circle to pass through the point and touch the circle (two cases). (In the first case, bisect line joining centre and point. In the second case, draw a second circle as first with P as centre, join centres and bisect.)

11. In an angle of 50°, draw the locus of a point which is always twice as far from one arm as it is from the other. (Draw parallels as shown from each arm 2:1 to plot locus.)

12. Draw the locus of a point which is always equidistant from a line and a semicircle. (Parallels from a straight line; arcs from centre of semicircle.)

13. Design a cam to give a three-second lift of 12 mm twice per revolution, one pause being twice the other between lifts. (Draw the base circle and 120° divisions first.)

14. Plot the locus of P at the end of the hanging link in the mechanism shown. (Draw the links in place, plot six points.)

15. Draw the ellipse when half the major axis is 40 mm, and a focal point 12 mm from the end of the m.a. (Draw the major axis; half the m.a. swung from the focal points gives minor axis.)

16. An ellipse has the major axis and minor axis in the ratio of 4:3. Draw the ellipse when the major axis is 100 mm. Draw normal and a tangent at 25 mm from the end of the m.a. (Draw by the two circle method, join P to focal points. Bisect angle.)

17. Enlarge the shape in the ratio of 6:5. (Draw radials from corner point.)

18. Decrease the given figure by one-quarter. Copy the figure twice the printed size. (Pole method.)

19. A scale, to measure ·01 mm which 100 mm represents 40 mm, is to be increased 1:1·6. Draw the scale. (Increase base by ratio and draw diagonal scale.)

20. Draw any irregular quadrilateral in a circle of 100 mm diam. Find the centre of gravity of a quadrilateral. (Draw the circle and the quadrilateral. Draw its diagonals, and draw the medians of the four triangles. Join intersections to give C. of G.)

21. A hexagon of 30 mm side falls to lose one-third of its height, reduce the projected area to a square of equal area. (Project area, reduce by mean proportional.)

22. A semicircle is wrapped round the cylinder, ends meeting. (Project the semicircle around the cylinder as shown.)

23. The elevation of a cut cylinder, diam. 40 mm is given. Make the development. (Project twelve generators.)

24. Two views of a triangle inclined to both V.P. and H.P. Obtain the true size of the triangle. Draw twice printed size. (Project the true length of the perpendicular of the triangle, to give the true apex.)

25. The plan of a line is given, whose true length is 50 mm. Draw the elevation. Draw the traces of the plane which contains the line. (Draw the plan, swing to V.P. Project 50 mm arc to meet projector from plan, to give elevation.)

26. A right square pyramid lies with its axis parallel to the H.P. and its base at 60° to the V.P. Draw the projections. 55 mm altitude, 35 mm base.

27. A square, whose diagonal is equal to half the circumference of a cylinder, is wrapped on the cylinder. Project the elevation.

28. Draw the helices of two points, one which travels twice as fast as the other along a cylinder 70 mm in diameter.

29. A vertical right cylinder interpenetrates a horizontal triangular prism. Draw three orthographic views and half cylinder development.

30. A right hexagonal prism angled at 60° interpenetrates a triangular prism. Draw two elevations and part development of the hexagonal prism.

31. A cylinder is interpenetrated by a square prism coaxially and at right angles. Project a plan and relative front elevation to the XY line, also part development of prism and hole in cylinder.

32. An hexagonal pyramid is cut by two inclined planes. Draw three ortho views of the portion of the pyramid below the cutting planes.

33. A circle is 50 mm in diameter. Find the circumference by graphical means. See 104.

34. The circumference of a circle is 160 mm. Find the diameter by graphical method. See 105.

35. A straight line is 70 mm long. Cut off an arc equal in length to the line when its radius is 60 mm. See 106.

36. An arc has a radius of 70 mm and subtends an

angle of 70°. Show graphically how to obtain a straight line equal in length to the arc. See 107.

37. A sector of a circle has a radius of 90 mm and subtends an angle of 150°. A straight line joins the ends of the arc. The whole shape represents the development of a cone. Project the elevation and plane of the cone. See 219.

38. Draw the development of the surface of an oblique cone, whose base diameter is 60 mm, altitude 80 mm, axis line 60° to the X Y line. See 186.

39. Draw the development of an oblique hexagonal pyramid whose base is bounded by a circle of 70 mm diameter, an altitude of 70 mm, and whose axis has an inclination of 70° to the H.P. See 185.

40. Find by graphical method, the centre of gravity of a square of 80 mm side, which has a portion removed by a line drawn from one corner to a point 30 mm from an adjacent corner. See 109.

41. Draw each of the motions shown in 135 twice or three times the printed size. Plot the middle

point of the link in A, B, C, E, H. Plot the locus of D in D, D in F, for one revolution.

42. A cam is made from a circle 50 mm diam., and drilled 10 mm offset from its centre. Plot the performance of the follower during one revolution. (130)

43. Draw the cam shown in 130, twice the printed size. Plot the performance graph.

44. Using the form shown in E, 129, plot the locus of a point on the circumference of the rolling circle, beginning at the low zero point of the circle.

45. Draw the rectangular hyperbola shown in 127. Plot the locus on the perimeter of a circle 30 mm diam. which rolls for one revolution on the curve.

46. Draw by graphical means, the area of a circle of 90 mm diam. which is pierced by a circle of 20 mm radius, midway on the radius of the larger circle.

47. Find the centre of gravity of a square of 70 mm side which has had a square removed from one corner of 25 mm side.

48. An arc is part of a circle of 60 mm radius, subtended by an angle of 70°. Draw a straight line equal in length to the arc. (107)

49. A straight line is 75 mm long. Draw an arc of 75 mm radius equal in length to the line. (106)

50. Find the square root of 6 graphically. (84)

51. Using 96, draw a suitable re-entrant polygon and reduce it to square of equal area.

52. Using the pole method in 87, reduce a suitable polygon in the ratio of 3:5.

53. Draw a freehand irregular shape as in 80, in a rectangle 100 mm by 70 mm, and find its area by Simpson's Rule. Find the area by the graphic method shown in 112, and compare the results.

54. A square turns without slipping inside a circle. Plot the locus of one corner, when the circle is 90 mm diam., and the side of the square is 30 mm.

55. A circle rolls inside an ellipse. Plot the locus of a point on the perimeter of the circle which is 30 mm diam., and the axes of the ellipse are 120 mm and 70 mm.

PROBLEMS

1. A right cone, 60 mm diam. base, height 70 mm, is pierced by the largest cylindrical hole possible parallel to the base. Draw a plan and two elevations full size using third angle projection. Draw also the development of the cone.

2. The oblique cone shown in No. 186 stands on an inclined plane which is at 30° to the H.P. Draw twice the shown size and using first angle projection, a plan and two elevations. Omit the section lines.

3. An oblique solid, height 60 mm, base shape elliptical, axes 70 mm and 40 mm, axis inclined at 60° to H.P., stands on the H.P., and is cut by an inclined plane to give the greatest area of section. Draw the plan and two elevations, F.S. using first angle project the true shape of the section.

4. A plate cam is elliptical in profile, axes 60 mm and 35 mm. Draw the performance graph of the cam, 1 rpm, using 120 mm to represent 60 secs.

5. An arc, radius 50 mm, is subtended by an angle

of 50°. Draw a straight line equal in length to that of the arc. Check by calculation.

6. The largest elliptical label is applied to a right cylinder height 60 mm and 70 mm diam. Draw F.S. first angle, the plan and two elevations of the assembly. Show the true shape of the label.

7. A solid of revolution is described by an equilateral triangle of side 30 mm on an overall radius of 45 mm to produce a ring form. The solid lies on the H.P. and is cut by an inclined plane 10° to the H.P. and passing through the centre point of the axis. Draw, F.S. third angle, a plan and two elevations of the solid. Hatch the cut face.

8. A right cone, base diameter 70 mm and height 50 mm, is penetrated by a vertical hexagonal prism of 15 mm side and 50 mm height. Both stand on the H.P., co-axial. Draw F.S. and using third angle projection, a plan and two elevations; develop the surface of both cone and prism.

9. An oblique cylinder height 50 mm, base dia-

meter 60 mm, axis at 60° to the H.P. is pierced co-axially by a square hole of 40 mm side. An inclined plane cuts the solid to give the largest section area. Draw F.S. first angle, a plan and two elevations and project the true shape of the section.

10. Draw the plan and sectional elevation of a nut which fits a bolt of 60 mm diam., square thread 16 mm pitch single start.

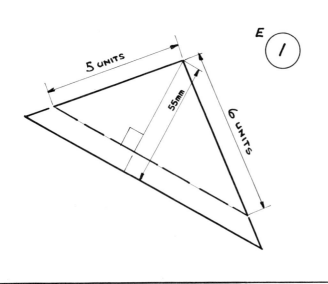

5 UNITS

55mm

6 UNITS

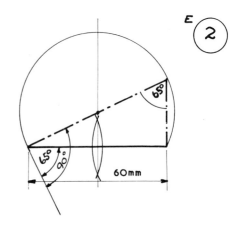

65°

65° 90°

60mm

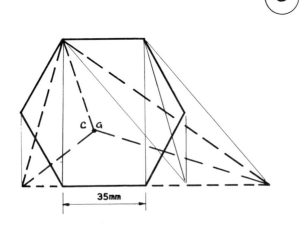

C G

35mm

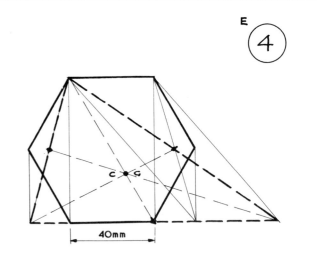

C G

40mm

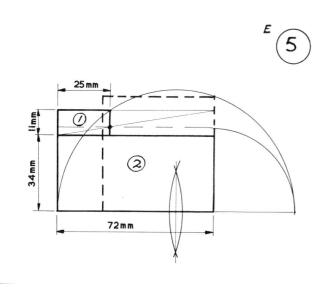

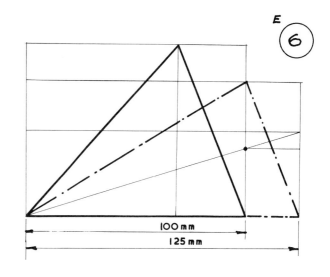

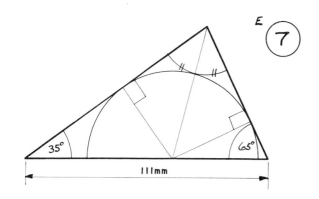

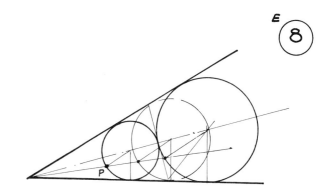

183

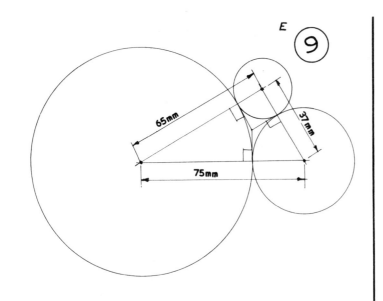

E 9

65mm

37mm

75mm

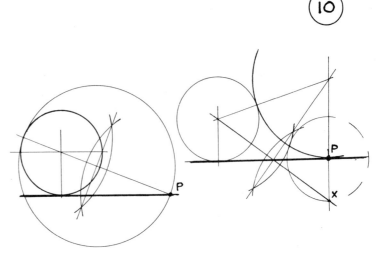

E 10

P

P

x

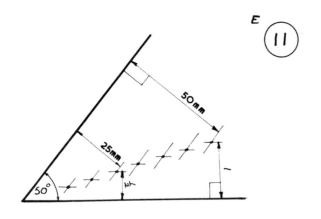

E 11

50mm

25mm

50°

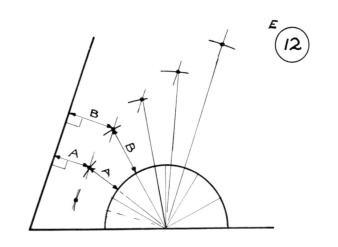

E 12

B

B

A

A

184

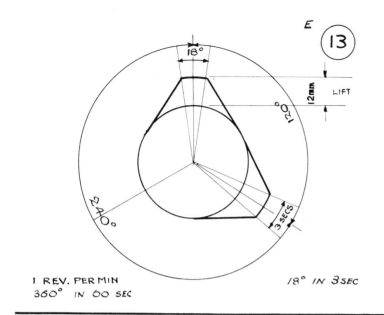

E (13)

18°

12mm LIFT

120°

240°

3 SECS

1 REV. PER MIN
360° IN 60 SEC

18° IN 3 SEC

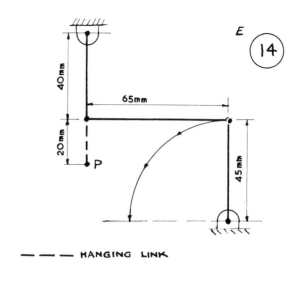

E (14)

40mm

65mm

20mm

P

45mm

— — — HANGING LINK

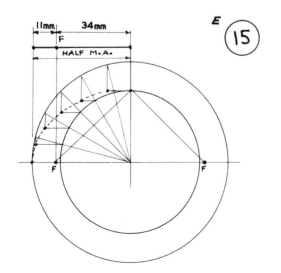

E (15)

11mm 34mm

F

HALF M.A.

F F

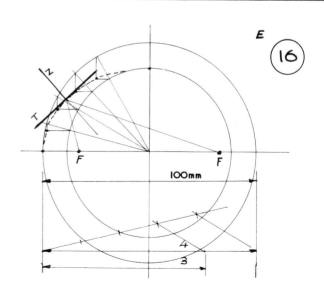

E (16)

N

T

F F

100mm

4

3

185

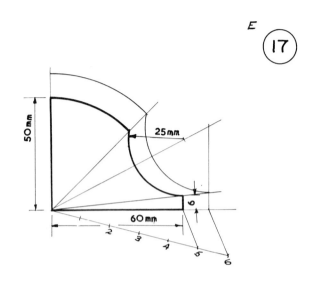

E (17)

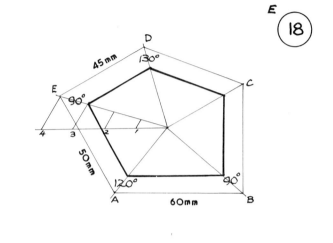

E (18)

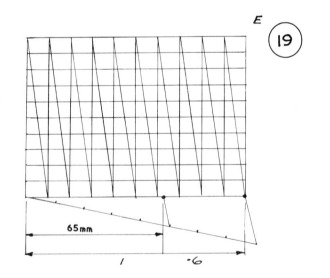

E (19)

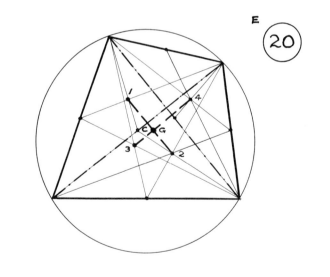

E (20)

186

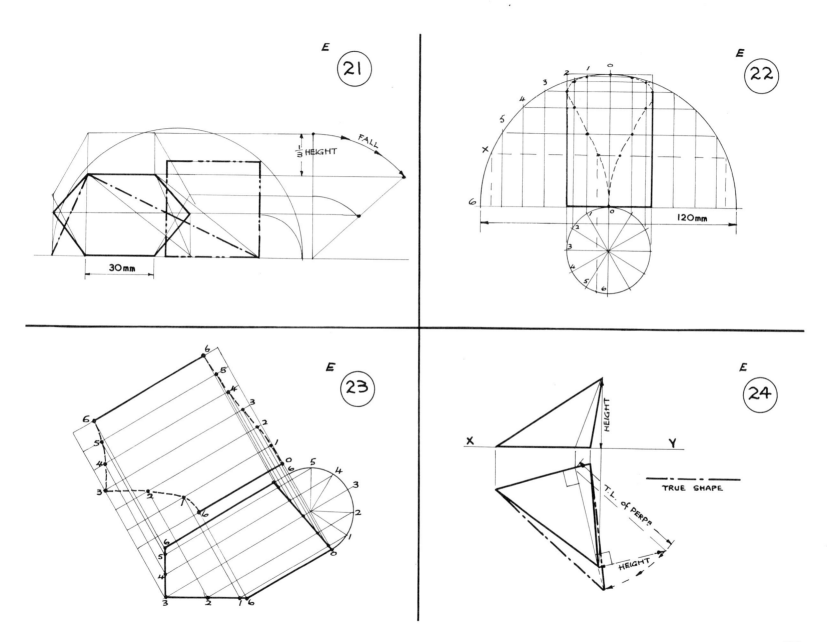

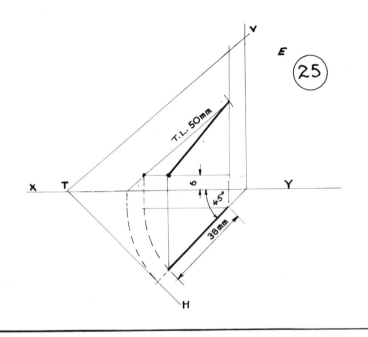

E (25)

V

T.L. 50mm

45°

38mm

X ——— T ————————————— Y

H

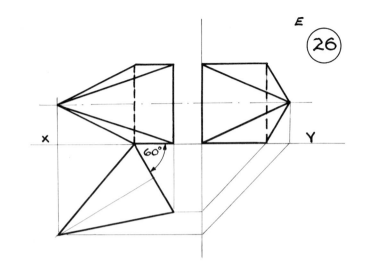

E (26)

X ————————————————— Y

60°

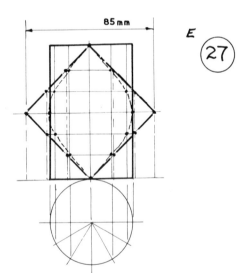

85mm

E (27)

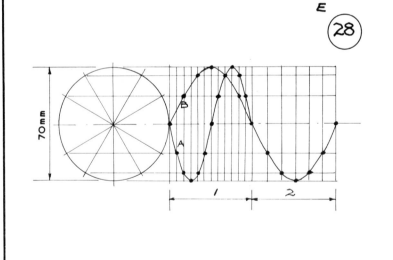

E (28)

70mm

A

B

1   2

188

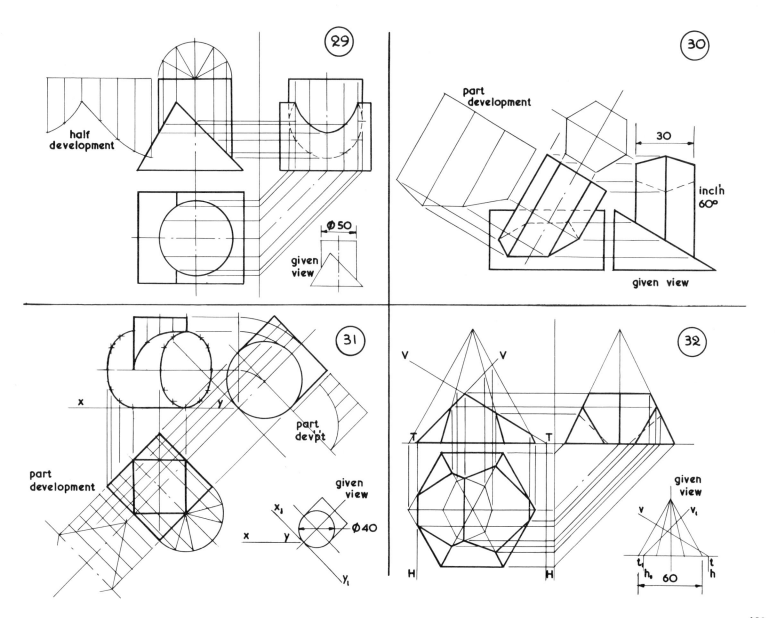

29

half
development

Ø50

given
view

30

part
development

30

incl'h
60°

given view

31

x

y

part
dev'pt

part
development

given
view

x₁

x   y

Ø40

y₁

32

V   V

T   T

H   H

given
view

v   v₁

t₁   t
h₀   h

60

189

Index

Numbers in the index refer to sections in the text